Pearson Education Limited
Edinburgh Gate
Harlow
Essex CM20 2JE
England
and Associated Companies throughout the world.

www.pearsonlongman.com

Eighth impression 2022

ISBN: 978-1-4082-4985-7

Set in VagRounded Infant

Printed by CPI UK

Acknowledgements
The publisher would like to thank the following for their kind permission to reproduce their photographs:

(Key: b-bottom; c-centre; l-left; r-right; t-top)

Alamy Images: CountrySideCollection - Homer Sykes 94; **Fotolia.com:** Andreas Gradin 108r; **Getty Images:** Phil Cole 85t, National Geographic / Mike Theiss 22r, US Coast Guard / Kyle Niemi 22l; **iStockphoto:** Steve Debenport 61r, fazon1 46tc, Joshua Hodge Photography 108l; **Lebrecht Music and Arts Photo Library:** Museum of Fine Arts, Boston 13t, 13b; **NASA:** 71; **Pearson Education Ltd:** Jon Barlow 10, 93, Trevor Clifford 9, 83; **Pearson Education Ltd:** Gareth Boden 61l, Peter Evans 46bl, Getty Images / Photodisc 22cr, Imagestate / Michael Duerinckx 46tl, Photodisc / StockTrek 22cl; **Rex Features:** 46br, East News 85b; **Shutterstock.com:** photogl 46tr, Ian Scott 109

All other images © Pearson Education

Every effort has been made to trace the copyright holders and we apologise in advance for any unintentional omissions. We would be pleased to insert the appropriate acknowledgement in any subsequent edition of this publication.

Illustrated by Diego Diaz/Lemonade Illustration; Sean Longcroft; Stephanie Strickland; Jurgen Ziewe/Debut Art; Dan Chernett/The Bright Agency

Yazoo 4
Activity Book

1a Where's Toto?

1 Write the questions and answers.

1 __Is__ Dr Wild an animal detective? __Yes, she is.__ **4** _____ Toto a cat? _____
2 _____ Oscar friendly? _____ **5** _____ Toto in the zoo? _____
3 _____ Kelly and Jack friends? _____ **6** _____ Kelly and Jack helpful? _____

2 Label the picture. Then choose and write.

~~Dr Wild~~ Oscar Jack Kelly Toto
niece nephew ~~toucan~~ detective

a __Dr Wild__ b _____ c _____ d _____ e _____

1 Toto is a ____toucan____ .
2 Dr Wild is an animal _____ .

3 'Jack is my _____,' says Dr Wild.
4 'Kelly is my _____,' says Dr Wild.

3 Look, choose and write. Then match.

clever ~~lazy~~ helpful friendly

a __He's lazy.__ b _____ c _____ d _____

1 (My mark for the English test is 10 out of 10. __c__)   3 (I don't want to go to school. _____)
2 (Can I clean the board, please? _____)   4 (Hello! You look great today. _____)

4 Choose and write the correct form.

stay help play eat drink ~~work~~ find

Dr Wild (1) ___works___ at home.
She (2) _____ missing animals. Jack and Kelly
(3) _____ with their aunt every summer. They
(4) _____ their aunt with her work. They (5) _____ games with Oscar, too. Oscar
(6) _____ lots of fish and he
(7) _____ milk every day.

5 Correct the sentences. Use don't or doesn't.

1 Jack and Kelly stay with their grandma every summer.
_____No, they don't stay with their grandma every summer._____

2 Dr Wild works in a zoo.
_____

3 Dr Wild finds missing cars.
_____

4 The children do their homework with Oscar.
_____

5 Oscar eats lots of salad.
_____

6 Oscar drinks orange juice every day.
_____

6 Circle and answer about you.

1 (Do) / Are you like books   Yes, I do. / No, I don't.
2 Do / Are you friendly?   _____
3 Do / Are you lazy?   _____
4 Do / Are you think you're helpful? _____
5 Do / Are you play a sport every day? _____

5

1b We're getting ready!

1 Label the picture. Then listen and write True or False. •))

can opener   compass   binoculars   passports   torch   ~~diary~~   laptop

1. diary
2. _____
3. _____
4. _____
5. _____
6. _____
7. _____

1 _____True_____   2 _____   3 _____   4 _____

2 Choose and write.

swimsuits   ball   pencil   sun cream   boots   oranges   tomatoes   cheese   apples   bread   ~~books~~

1 I want to do my homework. I need my ____books____ and a _____ .

2 My brother wants to play football. He needs a _____ and some _____ .

3 We want to make some juice. We need _____ and _____ .

4 My mum wants to make a sandwich. She needs some _____ , _____ and _____ .

5 My friends want to go to the beach. They need _____ and _____ .

3 Look, read and write the names.

1 They're wearing shorts, they're playing and they're laughing. _Gemma and Penny_

2 They're cooking and singing. _____

3 He's wearing shorts and he's drinking. _____

4 She's wearing jeans and she's sleeping. _____

5 He's reading and eating. _____

4 Look at 3 and answer.

1 What's Katy doing?

_____ She's sleeping. _____

2 Is Jim drinking?

_____

3 Are Penny and Gemma laughing?

_____

4 What's Ken wearing?

_____

5 What are Ken and Mary cooking?

_____

6 What's Jim eating?

_____

7 Is Gemma wearing a skirt?

_____

5 Look at 3 and correct the sentences.

1 Tom is drinking milk. _____ Tom is drinking water. _____

2 Katy is wearing a sweater. _____

3 Mary and Ken are eating burgers. _____

4 Jim is writing a book. _____

1 **Choose and write.**

boat ~~road~~ bad stop feather Toto

Dr Wild and the children drive along a (1) _____road_____ . Then Kelly sees a black (2) _____
in the road so they (3) _____ the car. Toto has black feathers and they think it's his feather.
Dr Wild looks through her binoculars at two people on a small (4) _____ . Their names are
Claudia and Magnus and they have got (5) _____ . Dr Wild says they're very
(6) _____ people. Dr Wild and the children need to find a boat!

2 **Do the crossword. Write the adverbs.**
Then complete the sentence with the secret word.

```
              2                    5      6  4
              □                    □      □
              □              3  4  □      □
       1      □              □  □  □      □
       h      □              □  □  □
   2   a  □ □ □ □ □ □ □ □ □ □ □ □ □ □ □ □
       p      □              □  □  □
       p      □              □  □  □
       i      □                 □  □
       l      □                 □  □
       y                        □
```

Do this crossword _____ !

3 **Match. Then choose and write.**

happily   slowly   ~~quickly~~   quietly

1 It's raining!
2 My dad's car is very old.
3 Ssh! The baby is sleeping.
4 My little sister loves her new ball.

a She's playing _____ .
b Let's run home __quickly__ .
c He drives _____ .
d Talk _____ .

4 **Look, circle and write adverbs from 2.**

1 The monkeys is / are eating ___quickly___ .

2 The acrobat is / are walking _____ .

3 The girls is / are laughing _____ .

4 The dancer is / are dancing _____ .

5 The clown is / are dancing _____ .

6 The boy is / are speaking _____ .

7 The horses is / are running _____ .

5 **Read and complete.**

eat my breakfast	do my homework	tidy my bedroom	play football
quickly			

Hi, I'm Rory. I don't eat my breakfast slowly. I eat it quickly. I don't want to be late for school! I don't do my homework quickly. I do it carefully. I don't want to make mistakes. I tidy my bedroom slowly. It's not fun! I love football. I play football well.

6 **Write about you.**

1 happily ___I play with my friends happily.___

2 carefully _____

3 slowly _____

4 quickly _____

5 badly _____

6 well _____

9

1d Let's phone Mel.

SKILLS

Writing class: punctuation

Look!
Has Mel's brother got a bike, a watch and rollerblades? Yes, he has.

1 **Correct the sentences. Add the punctuation.**

1 my name is kit baker ___My name is Kit Baker.___

2 im 11 years old and i live in bristol _____

3 im not very tall and ive got short brown hair

_____

4 ive got a big family my mum my dad two brothers and one sister

_____

5 at the moment im doing my english homework

_____

6 what do you do at the weekends _____

2 **Match. Then answer about you.**

1 What's your name?

2 How old are you?

3 What do you look like?

4 Where do you live?

5 What's your family like?

6 What do you do at the weekends?

7 What do you think you do well?

a At the weekends I like _____ .

b I think I _____ well.

c I've got a _____ family, my _____ .

d I live in _____ .

e I'm _____ old.

f My name is _____ .

g I'm _____ and I've got _____ eyes and _____ hair.

3 **What about you?** **Write a composition.**

Write about
• what you look like.
• your family.
• what you do at the weekends.

All about me!

_____
_____
_____
_____
_____

4 Read and circle.

1 eight, nine, double one, oh, three   **a** 890113   **b** (891103)
2 six, double five, seven, double two   **a** 655722   **b** 677522
3 oh, three, oh, nine, four, one   **a** 030941   **b** 033940
4 double eight, five, four, three, oh   **a** 855430   **b** 885430

5 Read and write the numbers.

1 oh, five, seven, double six, two   _057662_

2 four, double one, oh, three, six   _____

3 double seven, nine, two, oh, one   _____

6 Match.

1 Let's phone   **a** number?
2 What's her phone   **b** you doing?
3 Where   **c** Beth.
4 What are   **d** soon!
5 Do you want to   **e** come to my house later?
6 See you   **f** are you?

7 Look and write.

Danny

Max

Danny: Hi, (1) _____ Max _____ .

Max: Hello, Danny.

Danny: (2) _____

Max: I'm in town.

Danny: (3) _____

Max: I'm buying a T-shirt.

Danny: (4) _____
for a pizza later?

Max: Yes, great!

Danny: OK, see you soon.

Max: Bye!

Music

1 **Label the picture.**

bagpipes   composer   blow   ~~tango~~   opera   didgeridoo   polonaise

1 __tango__
2 _____
3 _____
4 _____
5 _____
6 _____
7 _____

2 **Write words from 1.**

1 The ____tango____ is an Argentinian dance.

2 Actors sing and dance in Chinese _____ .

3 A _____ is a very long loud instrument.

4 You _____ into Scottish _____ .

5 The _____ is a slow Polish dance.

6 A _____ writes music.

3 **Read and correct one word.**

1 The polonaise is a slow ~~instrument~~.   ____dance____

2 It's easy to play the didgeridoo.   _____

3 There are lots of drums and guitars in Chinese opera music.   _____

4 You sometimes run the tango quickly, sometimes slowly.   _____

5 Bagpipes are quiet instruments.   _____

4 Read and circle.

All over the world people like to play, sing and dance to music. Some instruments, like drums, the piano and the guitar, are popular in many countries. But some instruments are very special and you don't hear them every day.

In Madagascar, an island next to Africa, people like the music of the stick zither. It's an old instrument; it's long and thin and it's made of wood. The music is sometimes loud and sometimes quiet and you play it with your hands.

You don't play the wind harp with your hands and you don't blow it either. People don't play it; the wind plays it! You put this instrument in the garden or by a window. The wind blows and the harp makes a beautiful sound. It doesn't make a loud noise; it plays very quietly.

1 The piano, drums and the guitar are …
  a special. **b** popular.

2 The stick zither is …
  a from Madagascar. **b** always loud.

3 You play the stick zither …
  a in Africa. **b** with your hands.

4 … the wind harp.
  a People play **b** The wind plays

5 … always makes a quiet noise.
  a The stick zither **b** The wind harp

5 **Your project!** Answer about you.
Then design a CD cover for your favourite song.

1 What's your favourite instrument?

_____

2 Can you play an instrument?

_____

3 Where do you listen to music?

_____

4 What's your favourite song?

_____

2a There was a storm.

1 Read and circle.

Kelly: Where are Claudia and Magnus?

Jack: They're in that boat (1) in front of / in front us.

Kelly: Look at those big black (2) cloud / clouds in the sky.

Jack: It's very (3) wind / windy.

Kelly: Oh, no! (4) It's raining. / It raining.

Dr Wild: (5) I'm worried. / I'm a worry. Let's go inside. It's safe there.

2 Look, choose and write.

in front of   in   behind   next to

①  ②  ③  ④

The cat is ___in___ the boat.

The cat is _____ the boat.

The cat is _____ the boat.

The cat is _____ the boat.

3 Complete. Then look, choose and write.

Noun	Adjective
cloud	cloudy
rain	
	snowy
	stormy
sun	
wind	

1 There's lots of ____snow____ .

2 It's _____ .

3 There's a big black _____ in the sky.

4 It's _____ .

5 It's _____ .

6 There's a _____ with thunder and lightning.

4 **Look and write** was, wasn't, were **or** weren't.

Yesterday Claudia and Magnus (1) _____were_____ on a boat. Toto (2) _____ on the boat, too. In the night there (3) _____ a terrible storm with thunder and lightning. There (4) _____ lots of rain but Claudia and Magnus (5) _____ worried – the boat (6) _____ big and they (7) _____ inside in a warm room. Only Toto (8) _____ outside all night. In the morning his feathers (9) _____ very wet. He (10) _____ happy.

5 **Look, circle and answer.**

1 (Was)/ Were **there a boat?**   Yes, there was.   **4** Was / Were **there any rain?** _____

2 Was / Were **there any birds?** _____   **5** Was / Were **there any clouds?** _____

3 Was / Were **there any children?** _____   **6** Was / Were **there a man in the boat?** _____

6 **Write about yesterday for you. Use** was, wasn't, were **or** weren't.

1 It/cold and rainy. The weather/good.   _____

2 There/a storm in the evening. It/a bad night.   _____

3 My friends and I/at school. It/a holiday.   _____

4 My parents/at home in the evening. They/out.   _____

5 Yesterday/a busy day. There/lots to do.   _____

1 **Listen and tick the correct pictures.** •))

1

(a)

2

(c)

3

(e)

(b)

 ✔

(d)

Rabbits for sale

(f)

2 **Match with the pictures in 1.**

_____ aquarium   _____ café   _____ museum

_a_ town hall   _____ police station   _____ pet shop

3 **Read and write words from 2.**

1 I'm at the _police station_ and I'm asking a police officer for help.

2 They're looking at the old musical instruments in the _____ .

3 There's a concert in the _____ tonight.

4 We're looking at the fish in the _____ .

5 The children are playing with the rabbits in the _____ .

6 There are lots of different cakes in the _____ .

4 Look and match.

| 1 | 2 | 3 | 4 |

1 Yesterday morning	they helped	dinosaurs	in the museum.
2 Yesterday afternoon	they looked	on the swings	at home.
3 Yesterday evening	they painted	at the stars	in the park.
4 Last night	they played	their mum	in the sky.

5 Write and match.

1 Yesterday afternoon Kelly and Jack ____walked____ (walk)   **a** the museum.

2 In the library they _____ (look)   **b** to the library.

3 Then they _____ (visit)   **c** TV.

4 They _____ (ask)   **d** at the books.

5 Then they _____ (play)   **e** about the dinosaurs.

6 In the evening they _____ (watch)   **f** with Oscar.

6 Look, choose and write.

clean the bucket   drop her ice cream   ~~paint a picture~~   jump in the sea

1 ____She painted a picture.____

2 _____

3 _____

4 _____

Did you talk to them?

1 **Choose and write.**

wavy ~~toucan~~ tall blond follow beard sees

A boy tells Kelly and Jack about a man and woman with a (1) _____toucan_____ in a car. He says the man was short with a (2) _____ moustache and a (3) _____ . The woman was (4) _____ with (5) _____ hair. The boy (6) _____ the car again and shows Kelly and Jack. They (7) _____ the car.

2 **Look, choose and write.**

nose moustache blue face beard ~~blond~~ thin

This is Fred. He's got wavy (1) _____blond_____ hair and (2) _____ eyes. He's got a small (3) _____ and a (4) _____ mouth. He's got a (5) _____ but he hasn't got a (6) _____ . He's got a friendly (7) _____ .

3 **Read, look and complete.**

Katy   Ollie   Lucy

Name	Katy		
Nationality			
Personality		friendly	

The person with a thin face was Katy.

The person with a big smile was friendly.

The person with a diary was French.

The person with binoculars was English.

The person with a moustache and beard was Ollie.

The person wearing glasses was helpful.

The person with wavy blond hair was Lucy.

The person with a small nose was kind.

The person with a torch was Polish.

4 Write the opposite sentences.

1 Kelly showed the boy a photo of Oscar. <u>Kelly didn't show the boy a photo of Oscar.</u>

2 A car stopped near Kelly in the morning. _____

3 The boy noticed a cat in the car. _____

4 The boy looked at Magnus. _____

5 The boy didn't talk to Kelly and Jack. _____

6 They followed the boy. _____

5 Read and write.

Yesterday morning Paul (1) ____walked____ (walk) to the park where he

(2) _____ (wait) for his friend, Jess. They (3) _____

(climb) a tree and then they (4) _____ (argue). Jess

(5) _____ (want) to play with some other children but Paul

didn't. Jess and the children (6) _____ (play) football.

Paul (7) _____ (stay) and (8) _____ (watch) them for

ten minutes, then he (9) _____ (walk) home. On the way he

(10) _____ (talk) to a boy and a girl. They (11) _____

(ask) him some questions about a car and a toucan.

6 Look at 5 and answer.

1 Did Jess wait for Paul in the park? <u>No, she didn't.</u>

2 Did Jess and Paul climb a tree in the park? _____

3 Did Jess want to play with the other children? _____

4 Did Jess and Paul both play football? _____

5 Did Paul talk to a boy and a girl on the way home? _____

6 Did he ask them about a toucan? _____

7 Look at 5. Write questions and answers about yesterday.

1 Paul/walk to the park? <u>Did Paul walk to the park? Yes, he did.</u>

2 Jess and Paul/argue? _____

3 Paul/play with the other children? _____

4 the boy and girl/ask questions about Jess? _____

Writing class: paragraphs

 Choose and write to complete the paragraphs.

> I liked it but it was scary.
> It's red and white and it goes really fast.
> ~~I'm ten years old today.~~
> My family asked for chocolate cake but I wanted strawberry cake strawberry cake.

Look!

In the morning I cleaned my bedroom *and* helped my mum. Mum cooked lunch *and* I washed the dishes.

In the afternoon I walked to the park with my friend, Emma. We played tennis *but* I didn't play very well.

_____ **a** In the morning I opened my presents with my family. My favourite present was my new bike. It's fantastic.

_____

__1__ **b** **21st May.** It was hot and sunny today. It was a wonderful day. It's my birthday. <u>I'm ten years old today.</u>

_____ **c** In the evening it rained and we stayed at home. My dad cooked some chicken and pasta for dinner. Then we watched a detective film on TV. _____

_____

_____ **d** In the afternoon I visited the aquarium with my family. There were lots of fish. I liked the dolphins and the octopus but I didn't like the shark. There was a great café in the aquarium. _____

_____

2 **Number the paragraphs in 1 in order.**

3 **What about you?** **Write your diary for last Saturday.**

- Write what the weather was like.
- Write a paragraph about what you did in the morning.
- Write a paragraph about what you did in the afternoon.
- Write a paragraph about what you did in the evening.

> Saturday _____
>
> In the morning _____
>
> _____
>
> In the afternoon _____
>
> _____
>
> In the evening _____
>
> _____

4 **Number Danny's dialogue in order.**

a Yes, I'd like tickets for the museum, please. _____

b Two tickets, please. One adult and one child. _____

c Can I help you? __1__

d Thank you. _____

e The museum. Certainly. How many would you like? _____

f That's 12 euros. _____

5 **Choose and write.**

please   I'd like   tickets   ~~help~~   How many   Thank you

Ticket seller: Can I (1) _____ help _____ you?

Max: Yes, (2) _____ tickets for the cinema, (3) _____ .

Ticket seller: Certainly. (4) _____ would you like?

Max: Four (5) _____ , please. Four children.

Ticket seller: That's 16 euros.

Max: (6) _____ .

6 **Look at 4 and 5. Write Danny, Max or X.**

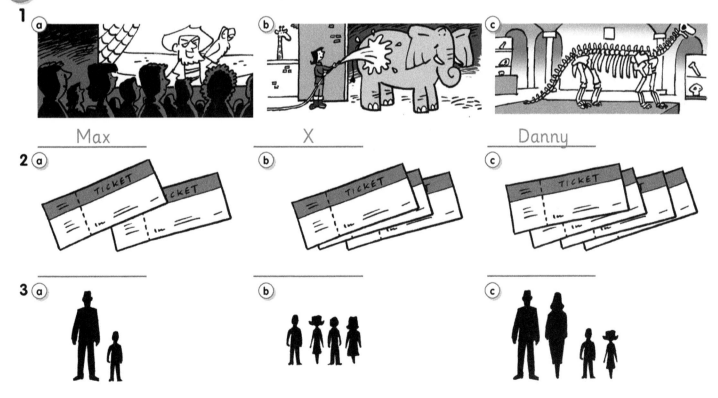

1
a _____ Max _____   b _____ X _____   c _____ Danny _____

2 a _____   b _____   c _____

3 a _____   b _____   c _____

4 a 9 euros   **b** 12 euros   **c** 16 euros

_____   _____   _____

Geography

1 Label the pictures.

hurricane ~~flood~~ tornado natural disaster

flood

_____

_____

_____

2 Read and circle.

1 Storms (produce) / rain about 1,000 tornadoes in the USA every year.

2 Tornadoes usually watch / last about four or five minutes.

3 More than 80 people die / wash in tornadoes every year.

4 Tornado winds can travel / stay at more than 400 kilometres an hour.

5 Tornadoes can come / destroy houses and trees.

3 Read, choose and write.

died   destroyed   travelled   floods   lasted   ~~hurricane~~

I remember a terrible (1) _____ when I was ten years old. It (2) _____ from Cuba to the USA. On August 17 1969 I watched it on TV. It was my tenth birthday. The name of the hurricane was Hurricane Camille. It (3) _____ nine days. The winds destroyed many houses, trees and cars and there were terrible (4) _____ . 256 people (5) _____ . We don't know how fast the winds were because the hurricane (6) _____ the weather instruments.

4 **Read and tick the things you need in a hurricane.**

Help! It's a hurricane!

Are you ready? Do you know what to do when a hurricane comes? It's summer and it's the hurricane season here in the USA. Do you live in the east of the country? This is the hurricane zone and you must plan what to do before a hurricane comes. You must choose a safe room in the house and have a bag ready. In the bag you need clothes, money, a mobile phone, a torch and a radio. You must also have food and water for a week. Do you have family or friends in other cities? Sometimes you must move to another city to be safe. You must think what to do with your pets when you go.

5 **Look at 4, read and circle.**

1 The hurricane season is in the   a spring.   **b** summer.   c winter.

2 People must   a watch the ocean.   **b** have a dog.   c make plans.

3 At home people must look for   a a big map.   **b** a safe room.   c good boots.

4 They need things to eat and drink for a   a week.   **b** month.   c year.

5 Sometimes people must go to another   a bed.   **b** city.   c country.

6 When people go to another place, they must think what to do with their   **a** car.   **b** camera.   c dog.

6 **Your project!** **Look and write.**

Day	Weather
Monday	☀
Tuesday	☁
Wednesday	🌧
Thursday	⛈
Friday	🌬

4–8 July

On (1) _____Monday_____ the weather was lovely. It was hot and
(2) _____sunny_____ .

On (3) _____ it was (4) _____ but it didn't rain.

On (5) _____ it (6) _____ all day.

On (7) _____ there was a terrible (8) _____ .

On (9) _____ the rain stopped but it was cold and there were strong (10) _____ coming from the north.

Review 1

1 **Read, draw and colour.**

 She's got long brown wavy hair. She wears glasses.

 He's got short black hair, a black moustache and a grey beard.

2 **Look and write questions and answers.**

1 PETS	**2** CINEMA	**3** MUSEUM

1 café   _Is she going to a café? No, she isn't. She's going to a pet shop._

sunny   _Is it sunny? No, it isn't. It's cloudy._

2 town hall   _____

rainy   _____

3 police station   _____

windy   _____

3 **Read, choose and write. Then circle.**

clever   friendly   ~~lazy~~   helpful

1 He's _____lazy_____ . He's getting up very (slowly)/ quickly.

2 She's _____ . She's talking happily / slowly.

3 They're _____ . They're tidying the bedroom carefully / sadly.

4 She's _____ . She's doing her homework very well / badly.

4 **Write and say.**

Yesterday I (1) _____walked_____ (walk) to the park to meet my friends. I was early so I

(2) _____ (wait) for them. We (3) _____ (play) in the playground and

(4) _____ (climb) a tree. Then we (5) _____ (watch) some people playing football.

5. Look and write questions and answers.

Amy yesterday

John yesterday

1. they/walk/to the park? ✓   Did they walk to the park yesterday? Yes, they did.
2. John/play tennis? ✗   Did John play tennis? No, he didn't. He played football.
3. Amy/climb a mountain? ✗ _____
4. the dog/jump in the pool? ✓ _____
5. they/listen to a band? ✓ _____
6. they/wash their hair? ✗ _____

My English

6. Look and write. Then check and answer.

Yesterday

Today

1. Yesterday there _____ a terrible storm. ☐

2. A man with a grey _____ watched the thunder and lightning. ☐

3. He _____ stay in the house. ☐

4. Today he's _____ quietly in the garden ☐

5. He's got his _____ with him. ☐

How did you do? _____   **1** = OK   **2–3** = Good   **4–5** = Excellent

Robinson Crusoe

1 Do the crossword.

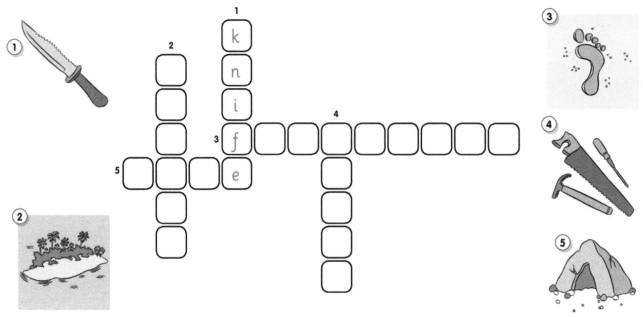

1. k
   n
   i
3. f e
5.

2 Number the pictures in order. Then read Read *Robinson Crusoe* on pages 28–29 of your Pupils' Book.

3 Look at 2, choose and write.

He makes a boat and gets tools, food and clothes from the ship.

It rains a lot and Robinson Crusoe is sad.

He makes a tent in a cave.

~~Robinson Crusoe leaves Brazil with ten other men.~~

There's a great storm at sea.

He sees a footprint on the beach.

He doesn't know where he is. He has no things.

He swims to the ship.

Picture 1: _____Robinson Crusoe leaves Brazil with ten other men._____

Picture 2: _____

Picture 3: _____

Picture 4: _____

Picture 5: _____

Picture 6: _____

Picture 7: _____

Picture 8: _____

4 Read and write True or False.

1 Robinson Crusoe wanted to go to the island. _____False_____

2 Ten men are lost in the sea. _____

3 Crusoe gets knives, food and water from the ship. _____

4 The weather is always sunny on the island. _____

5 He's sad in September because it's his birthday. _____

6 He knows who made the footprint on the beach. _____

5 Match the sentences with the same meaning.

1 I've got nothing with me.　　　　　　　　　　a The weather is stormy.

2 It leaves me on the beach.　　　　　　　　　　b The sea takes me to an island.

3 I make 11 journeys between the beach　　　　c I haven't got any food, clothes or tools.
  and the ship.

4 The wind and rain are strong all night.　　　　d I go to the ship lots of times in a small boat.

Magnus and Claudia had an accident!

3a

1 Read and circle.

1 Jack, Kelly and Dr Wild are looking for a blue (car) / cow.

2 Some cows are eating grass / Claudia.

3 Jack thinks an owl / a pond is making a noise.

4 Magnus crashed the car / bull into a tree.

5 Claudia and Magnus are in the duck / cow pond and they're wet.

6 The bull / duck is angry and it's chasing Magnus and Claudia.

2 Choose and write. Then match.

farm   grass   pond   owl   ~~bull~~   cow

a	b	c	d	e	f

1 __f__ This animal is big and sometimes it's angry: ____bull____

2 _____ Cows eat this; it's green: _____

3 _____ We get milk from this animal: _____

4 _____ Ducks sometimes swim here: _____

5 _____ Animals live here and farmers work here: _____

6 _____ This is a bird with big eyes; it flies at night: _____

3 Choose and complete.

to school   ~~a Maths test~~   some music on the radio   a funny film on TV   in the river   to the park
spaghetti for lunch   a good song   a white cat in the garden   off my bike

have	fall	go	see	hear
a Maths test				

4 Write **every day** or **yesterday**.

1 I go to school ___every day___ . I went to school ___yesterday___ .

2 I saw my friends _____ . I see my friends _____ .

3 My little brother is two years old. He falls over _____ . He fell over _____ .

4 I hear birds singing _____ . I heard birds singing _____ .

5 I had lots of homework _____ . I have lots of homework _____ .

6 My mum drove to work _____ . My mum drives to work _____ .

5 Read, choose and write.

My brother had a party   ~~We went to a museum~~   We heard a bird

I saw my grandma   My dad fell off a horse

1 ___We went to a museum___ yesterday. It was very interesting.

2 _____ on Saturday. It was his birthday.

3 _____ last night. It was an owl.

4 _____ yesterday. He wasn't happy.

5 _____ last weekend. She was very well.

6 Choose and write the correct form.

go   ~~drive~~   hear   see   have   fall

1 My teacher ___drove___ her new car to school yesterday.

2 My friend _____ in the river yesterday. He was wet!

3 We _____ an English test at school yesterday.

4 I _____ some lovely music on the radio yesterday.

5 My sister _____ to school by bike yesterday.

6 I've got binoculars and yesterday I _____ some beautiful birds.

7 Write about you.

1 This morning I ___had___ (have) _____ for breakfast.

2 Last night I _____ (hear) _____ .

3 Yesterday I _____ (see) _____ .

4 Last weekend my dad _____ (drive) _____ .

5 Last summer my family _____ (go) _____ .

6 When I was young, I _____ (fall) _____ .

1 Listen and match. 🔊

2 **Match with the pictures in 1. Then choose and write.**

unhappy   confused   nervous   ~~scared~~

_____ **a** The little boy is crying. He can't find his cat and he's _____ .

_____ **b** Lots of people are watching me. I can't sing. I'm very _____ .

___1___ **c** My sister is _____scared_____ of big dogs.

_____ **d** I don't know the answer to this question. Is it yes or no? I'm _____ .

3 **Choose and write.**

heard   nervous   confused   pond   fell   ~~farm~~   unhappy   scared   slowly

I went to a (1) _____farm_____ yesterday with my family. We saw some cows, sheep and bulls. My sister cried because she was (2) _____ of the animals. My dad drove an old car from the farm. The car was very difficult to drive and he was (3) _____ because he thought he might crash. He drove very (4) _____ ! There were lots of ducks in a (5) _____ . I (6) _____ a big splash. My brother (7) _____ in the pond! He was (8) _____ because the water was very cold … and the ducks looked (9) _____ when they saw him in their pond!

4 Read and number in order.

_1_ **a** My name's Jimmy and I didn't have a good day yesterday! I didn't wake up at seven o'clock. I didn't hear my alarm clock!

____ **b** I had lots of homework in the evening. I didn't know how to do my English homework. I was confused! I was happy when it was time for bed!

____ **c** At lunchtime it rained and we didn't go out to play. I looked in my bag but I didn't have my lunch box. I was hungry. My friend had two sandwiches but they fell on the floor.

____ **d** My mum didn't drive me to school. I ran but I was late for school and my teacher was unhappy.

____ **e** We had a Maths test in the morning and I was nervous. I didn't know three of the answers. I didn't do those questions.

5 Choose and write the questions. Then look at 4 and answer.

have   answer   have   go   ~~hear~~   have

1 __Did__ Jimmy _____ _hear_ _____ his alarm clock at seven?   _____ No, he didn't. _____

2 _____ he _____ to school by car?   _____

3 _____ he _____ a Maths test?   _____

4 _____ he _____ all the questions?   _____

5 _____ he _____ a sandwich for lunch?   _____

6 _____ he _____ homework in the evening?   _____

6 Write about your day yesterday.

1 see my teacher

I saw my teacher./I didn't see my teacher. _____

2 hear my alarm clock in the morning

_____

3 see my best friend

_____

4 go to school by bus

_____

5 have sandwiches for lunch

_____

6 have lots of homework

_____

1 **Read and correct one word.**

1 Magnus ~~have~~ a cold and a sore throat.   ___had___

2 He was hungry but he didn't eating the big sandwich. _____

3 Claudia was well – she had earache.   _____

4 Claudia not eat ice cream.   _____

5 Magnus watches TV.   _____

6 Toto were unhappy in his cage.   _____

2 **Look and match.**

①

②

③

④

⑤

⑥

_____ stomachache   _____ well   _____ cold

__1_ headache   _____ sore throat   _____ earache

3 **Look at 2. Write and circle.**

1 She had a __headache__ yesterday evening and she did / (didn't do) her homework.

2 He had a _____ yesterday and he went / didn't go to school.

3 She was _____ yesterday and she went / didn't go to the park on her bike.

4 He had _____ this morning and he had / didn't have breakfast.

5 She had _____ yesterday but she did / didn't do a puzzle.

6 He had a _____ yesterday so he talked / didn't talk to his friend.

4 **Write the opposite sentences.**

1 It was stormy. He didn't go out in his boat.   It wasn't stormy. He went out in his boat.

2 It wasn't cloudy. I took lots of photos.   _____

3 It was rainy. They didn't sit in the garden.   _____

4 It wasn't windy. We ate our lunch outside.   _____

5 It was sunny. She read her book in the park.   _____

6 It wasn't snowy. The children didn't make a snowman.   _____

5 **Look and write.**

Billy had stomachache yesterday. What did he do? What didn't he do?

1 go to school   _____ He didn't go to school. _____

2 stay in bed   _____

3 write a letter to his grandma   _____

4 make paper planes   _____

5 drink lots of water   _____

6 eat his dinner   _____

7 watch TV   _____

8 sleep in the afternoon   _____

6 **Answer about you.**

1 What did you eat for dinner yesterday?   _____

2 What did you drink for breakfast this morning?   _____

3 What book did you read last night?   _____

4 What did you do yesterday evening?   _____

3d

I'm sorry I didn't come.

Writing class: *on/in/at* with days and times

Look!
I went to a farm on Sunday. We went for a walk in the morning. My dad took me home at six o'clock.

 Choose and complete.

half past eleven   ~~Monday~~   the evening   Wednesday
twelve o'clock   Saturday   the morning   the afternoon
eight o'clock

on	in	at
Monday		

2 **Write in, on or at.**

(1) ___On___ Monday I went to school (2) _____ eight o'clock (3) _____ the morning.

I had a swimming lesson (4) _____ half past four (5) _____ the afternoon (6) _____ Tuesday.

I phoned my grandma (7) _____ seven o'clock (8) _____ the evening (9) _____ Sunday.

3 **What about you?** **Write a letter about last weekend.**

Write
• where you went.
• when you went.
• who you went with.
• one thing you saw.
• one thing you didn't do.

Dear _____ ,

_____

_____

_____

_____

_____

_____

With love from _____

4 Match.

1 I was
2 I had
3 Are you
4 Did you
5 What

a a headache.
b ill.
c happened?
d all right now?
e have a good time?

5 Number the dialogue in order.

a Yes, thanks. Did you have a good time? _____

b I was ill. I had a headache. _____

c Yes, it was great. _____

d Are you all right now? _____

e I'm sorry I didn't come to your party. _1_

f That's OK. What happened? _____

6 Look and write.

Annie: (1) _I'm sorry I didn't come to the cinema._
Sam: That's OK. What happened?
Annie: (2) _____
Sam: Are you all right now?
Annie: Yes, thanks. Did you have a good time?
Sam: Yes, it was great.

Clare: (3) _____
Ben: That's OK. What happened?
Clare: (4) _____
Ben: Are you all right now?
Clare: Yes, thanks. Did you have a good time?
Ben: Yes, it was great.

Technology

1 Label the pictures. Then circle the machines.

radio   ~~TV~~   mobile phone   computer   letter   e-book reader   newspaper

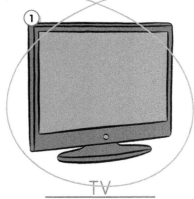
TV

_____

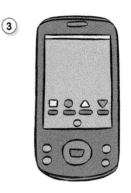
_____

_____

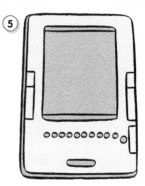
_____

_____

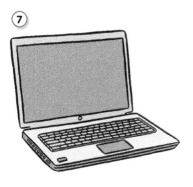
_____

2 Choose and write.

~~machines/communicate~~   size/room   weighed/appeared   clay/paper

1 We often use ___machines___ to _communicate_ with other people.

2 Before we had _____ , people wrote on _____ .

3 The first mobile phone _____ in 1973 and _____ two kilos.

4 The first computers were the _____ of a _____ .

3 Write about what you did or didn't do yesterday.

1 use a mobile phone I used a mobile phone yesterday./I didn't use a mobile phone yesterday.

2 watch TV _____

3 write an email _____

4 read an e-book _____

5 talk to a friend _____

6 listen to the radio _____

4 **Read and complete.**

People use computers at school, at home and at work. We use them to write emails, play games, go shopping and learn about the world. For all these things, we need the Internet. The Internet is a network of lots of different computers which communicate at the same time.

Millions of people use the Internet every day but it's only 40 years old. The first people went online in America in 1969. At first the Internet was small and there were only 37 computers online. It was difficult to use and there was no email. Queen Elizabeth II of the United Kingdom wrote one of the first emails in 1976. 13 years later, Tim Berners-Lee and his team in Switzerland started the World Wide Web. This made it easy for everyone to use the Internet. By 2011 there were two billion people online in the world. Today we can go online in any country in the world and we can use the Internet at any time of the day or night.

1969	People went online in America
	Email used for the first time
	The World Wide Web started
	2,000,000,000 people online in the world

5 **Look at 4. Read and answer.**

1 What do you need to go shopping on a computer? _____the Internet_____

2 What is the Internet? _____

3 How old is the Internet? _____

4 How many computers were online in 1969? _____

5 Who started the World Wide Web? _____

6 When can you go online? _____

6 **Your project!** Tick or cross the types of communication you use at school. **Then write.**

☐ e-book

☐ interactive whiteboard

☐ computer

☐ mobile phone

☐ TV

☐ CD player

☐ newspaper

Communication at school

At school we use _____

_____.

We use it to _____

_____.

My teacher uses _____

_____.

He/She uses it to _____

_____.

We also use _____

_____.

4a They went through the town.

1 Choose and write.

train station ~~photo~~ train newspaper on along bridge

Kelly saw Magnus in a (1) ____photo____ in the

(2) _____ . He was at the (3)

_____ . Dr Wild, Jack and Kelly walked

(4) _____ the road and across the

(5) _____ to the station. They saw Claudia

and Magnus getting on a (6) _____ .

They all got (7) _____ the train, too.

THIEF STEALS SUITCASE

2 Look and match.

castle ___4___   market _____   bridge _____

train station _____   hotel _____   road _____

3 Read and write words from 2.

1 I bought some strawberries and oranges in the ____market____ .

2 Last weekend we stayed in the _____ next to the museum.

3 King John lived in this _____ .

4 This is the _____ to London.

5 We didn't go across the river because a storm destroyed the _____ .

6 The _____ was very busy because there were lots of trains yesterday.

4 Read and draw the route. Then answer the question.

Claudia and Magnus are here

After a week Magnus and Claudia were better and ready to leave their hotel. They walked along the road. It was a hot day and Magnus was thirsty. He wanted a drink but they walked past the café. They didn't have time to stop for a drink.

They walked around the castle and across the bridge. Then they went past the hospital and through the park. Then they ran because they were late. They saw their train. Luckily they had their tickets because they bought them yesterday.

Where are they going? _____

5 Read and circle.

1 The dog walked across / around the road.

2 It ran along / through a forest.

3 It went on / past a house.

4 It went around / along a lake.

5 It walked along / past a river.

6 Choose and write about your journey to school.

along   past   through   across   around

1 I __go_____ .

2 I _____ .

3 I _____ .

1 Listen and number. •))

2 Look at 1, read and write True or False.

Picture a

1 There aren't any seats at the station. _____True_____

2 A boy is searching for his sister. _____

3 There are three trains. _____

4 There's some luggage at the station.
_____

Picture b

5 A woman is looking after a dog. _____

6 There are four carriages. _____

7 There are two people at the station.
_____

8 There's some luggage on the seats.
_____

3 Choose and write.

seat   carriages   ~~luggage~~   searching   look after   money

1 Please can you help me carry my ____luggage____ to the train station?

2 I sit next to my friend Penny at school. Her _____ is next to mine.

3 I sometimes _____ my little sister in the afternoons.

4 Those children can't find their dog and they're _____ for it in the park.

5 I'm going to the bank. I need some _____ .

6 It's a very long train. It's got ten _____ .

4 Look and write.

M = Mother   **D** = Daughter

shoes ✓ €40
binoculars ✓ €15
torch ✓ €8
sunglasses ✓ €12
guitar ✓ €35
watch ✓ €28

M: How much money did you have?   **D:** I had 150 euros.

M: (1) _How much were the shoes?_   **D:** _They were 40 euros._

M: (2) _____   **D:** _____

M: (3) _____   **D:** _____

M: (4) _____   **D:** _____

M: (5) _____   **D:** _____

M: (6) _____   **D:** _____

M: (7) How much money have you got now?   **D:** I've got _____ .

5 Read and draw the food and drink. Then write There's/There are.

1 ___There's___ some spaghetti.

2 _____ three eggs.

3 _____ some fish.

4 _____ some milk.

5 _____ five tomatoes.

6 _____ lots of juice.

6 Write. Then look and circle.

1 _How much_ luggage ___is there___ ?

(There's lots of luggage.)/ There are lots of luggage.

2 _How many_ seats _____ ?

There are lots of seats. / There aren't any seats.

3 _____ rain _____ ?

There's lots of rain. / There are lots of rain.

4 _____ people _____ ?

There isn't lots of people. / There are six people.

5 _____ clouds _____ ?

There's lots of clouds. / There are lots of clouds.

1 Look, read and circle.

1 Where are Claudia and Magnus?
   a on a train   **b** in a hotel

2 What are they doing?
   a They're sleeping.   **b** They're eating.

3 What's Magnus eating?
   a stew and rice   **b** trousers and a shirt

4 What can Claudia hear?
   a children and a cat   **b** loud music

5 What does Claudia want?
   a a new bag   **b** Oscar

2 Find, circle and write the six food words.

1   peas

2 _____

3 _____

4 _____

5 _____

6 _____

e	u	l	n	p	s	c
r	p	u	i	i	x	h
g	e	y	w	v	u	i
e	a	i	t	e	h	p
a	s	t	e	a	k	s
s	m	t	s	t	e	r
f	w	s	t	e	w	i
k	o	v	e	w	z	c
c	a	b	b	a	g	e

3 Look and answer.

1 What's the boy eating?
   He's eating stew, rice and cabbage.

2 What's the woman eating?
_____

3 What's the girl eating?
_____

4 What are they drinking?
_____

4 Look, choose and write questions. Use Is there much …?/Are there many …?

peas   cabbage   rice   ~~stew~~   steaks   chips

1 _____ *Is there much stew?* _____   4 _____

2 _____   5 _____

3 _____   6 _____

5 Look at 4 and match.

1 There isn't much __d__ _____   **a** steaks.   **d** ~~cabbage~~.

2 There are lots of _____   **b** peas.   **e** chips.

3 There aren't many _____ _____   **c** stew.   **f** rice.

4 There's lots of _____

6 Circle and write much/many.

There (1) is / are lots of stew but there (2) isn't / aren't (3) _____ peas. There (4) isn't / aren't

(5) _____ cabbage and there (6) isn't / aren't (7) _____ steaks. There (8) is / are lots of

rice but there (9) isn't / aren't (10) _____ chips.

7 Write.

✓ = lots of   ✗ = not much/many

1 meat ✗
_____ *There isn't much meat.* _____

2 biscuits ✓
_____

3 bananas ✗
_____

4 pasta ✓
_____

5 chocolate ✗
_____

6 carrots ✗
_____

4d

I'd like chips.

Writing class: *first, then, afterwards, finally* ✏️

 Write and match.

Afterwards   First   Finally   ~~Last week~~   Then

1 __Last week__ our class went to
2 _____ we walked around the
3 _____ we ate
4 _____ we visited
5 _____ we went

a lunch in a café.
b to the shop.
c the Great Park.
d castle.
e Windsor.

Look!

First we walked around the town. *Then* we ate lunch. *Afterwards* we walked in the park. *Finally* we went home.

 Look and correct the sentences.

1 Last month we went to London. __Last month we went to York.__

2 First we went to the museum and looked at the cars. _____

3 Then we had lunch in a café. _____

4 Afterwards we visited the library. _____

5 Finally we walked along the river. _____

③ **What about you?** Write a report about a school trip.

- Write about when and where you went.
- Write about these things in the order you did them: a place you visited, the food you ate, two activities you did.

Our school trip to _____
First _____
_____
Then _____
_____
Afterwards _____
_____
Finally _____
_____

4 Choose and complete.

cake ~~stew~~ milk chicken bananas carrots ice cream water steaks potatoes
orange juice peas cherries apples chocolate

Meat	Vegetables	Drinks	Fruit	Sweet
stew				

5 Read and circle.

A: What would you like?

B: I'd like stew, cabbage and rice, please.

1 ⓐ  ⓑ  ⓒ

A: And to drink?

B: I'll have orange juice, please.

2 ⓐ ⓑ ⓒ

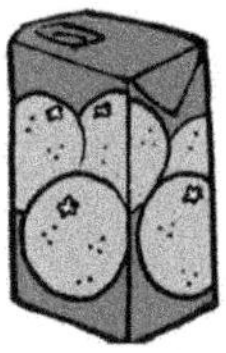

A: Would you like anything else?

B: Yes, I'd like chocolate cake, please.

A: Thank you.

3 ⓐ  ⓑ  ⓒ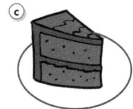

6 Read and write.

1 _What would you like?_ — I'd like chicken and salad, please.

2 _____ — I'll have milk, please.

3 _____ — Yes, I'd like strawberries, please.

Geography

1 **Choose and write.**

Big Wheel   crown   art gallery   ~~tower~~   church   palace   cathedral

1 This isn't a house but it's very tall: _____ tower _____ .

2 You can see lots of paintings here: _____ .

3 People often go to a _____ on Sundays.

4 It's fun to go on a _____ . You sit in a seat and go very high!

5 Kings and queens often live in a big house called a _____ .

6 The queen wears a _____ on her head on special days.

7 This is a very big church: _____ .

2 **Choose and write. Then number the pictures in order.**

~~cathedral~~   Big Wheel   River   art gallery

Tate Modern is an art gallery.

1

St Paul's is a cathedral.

The London Eye is a Big Wheel.

This is the River Thames

The Tower of London is very old.

Hi, I'm Eve. I went to London last month with my school. London is the capital of England. It's a beautiful city with lots of things to see and do. We went on a tour of the city. First we went to St Paul's. It's a beautiful (1) _____ cathedral _____ . Then we saw the Tower of London. There were lots of big black birds in the gardens. We also went for a ride on the London Eye. That is a famous (2) _____ with great views over the city. Afterwards we walked around Tate Modern. That is an (3) _____ . Finally we went on a boat along the (4) _____ Thames. We had a great time!

 3 **Read and label the map.**

Blackhorse Road   Sunny Bridge   Bushy Park   Whitewater River   ~~Green Street~~

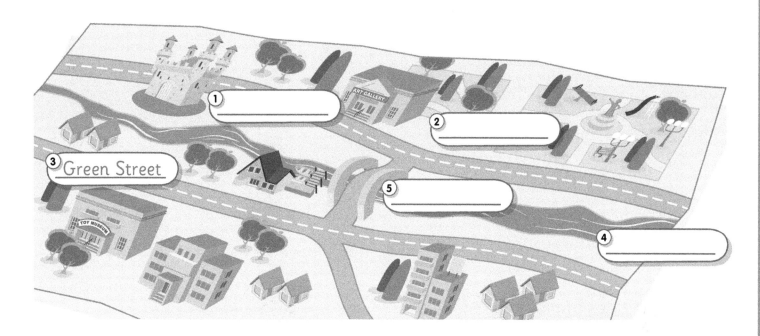

3 Green Street

Last weekend my friend and I walked around our town. First we went to the Toy Museum in Green Street. That was great. We saw lots of old dolls and cars there.

Then we went across Sunny Bridge to Blackhorse Road and went to the castle there. The castle has a very high tower.

Then we went to Bushy Park. There is an art gallery there with lots of nice paintings.

Finally we got on a boat and went along Whitewater River.

 4 **Your project!** **Choose and complete. Then write.**

Where did you go on holiday last summer?
Did you visit any interesting places?

castle   art gallery   church   cathedral

museum   palace   tower   park   river

Name of place	Type of attraction
The Louvre	art gallery

My holiday

I went to _____

last summer.

We visited a _____

there. It was called _____.

We also visited _____.

I thought it was _____.

My favourite place was _____.

Review 2

1 Choose and write. Then add your own words.

~~earache~~ money steak bull duck luggage castle nervous rice horse
cold museum owl scared

Your words

1 Illnesses	_earache_	
2 Places you can visit		
3 Farm animals		
4 Food		
5 Things you take on holiday		
6 Birds		
7 Feelings		

2 Look, choose and write.

~~stew~~ potatoes cabbage water peas

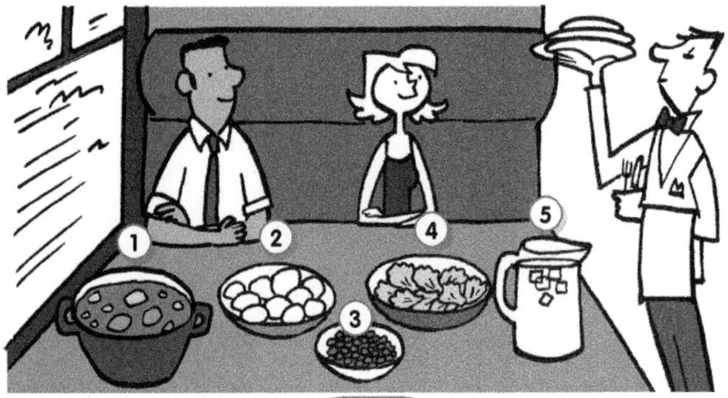

Before

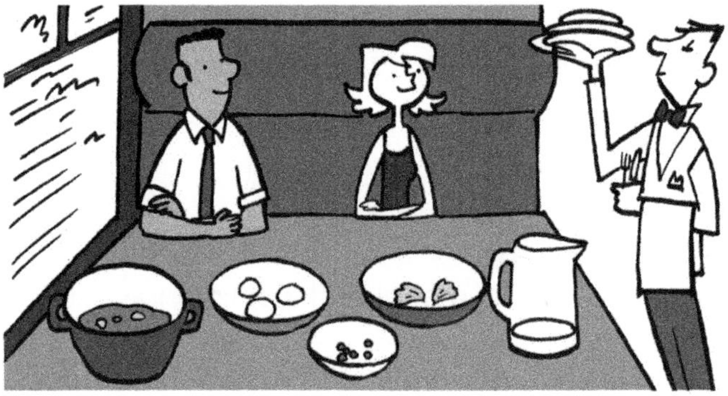

After

1 _There was lots of stew._   _There isn't much stew now._

2 _____   _____

3 _____   _____

4 _____   _____

5 _____   _____

3 Write wh, w or h and say.

(1) _Wh_ o (2) _____ as that (3) _____ oman and (4) _____y did she (5) _____ ear a (6) _____ite
(7) _____at? She (8) _____aited and (9) _____atched (10) _____appy (11) _____ales in the (12) _____ater!

4 Look and answer.

Stella and Max yesterday

1 Where did Stella and Max go yesterday? _____ They went to the zoo. _____

2 What animals did they see? _____

3 What did Max do? _____

4 What did they eat? _____

5 What did they drink? _____

6 What did they hear? _____

7 What did they have in their bag? _____

8 What did the penguins say to Max? (Guess!) _____

My English

5 Look and write. Then check and answer.

① ② ③ ④ ⑤

1 He had _____ . ☐

2 The dog ran _____ the tree. ☐

3 There isn't _____ money. ☐

4 She wasn't happy. She was

_____ ! ☐

5 He _____ lots of milk. ☐

How did you do? _____   **1** = OK   **2–3** = Good   **4–5** = Excellent

Alice in Wonderland

1 Choose and write.

hare ~~place~~ polite tea wide angrily wine

1 Where can I sit? There isn't a _____place_____ for me.

2 Sometimes my parents have a glass of red _____ with their dinner.

3 That's a very big rabbit. I think it's a _____ .

4 You must speak nicely to your teachers and be _____ .

5 I like milk and sugar in my cup of _____ .

6 When you're very surprised, you open your eyes _____ .

7 'No! You mustn't do that. You're a bad child!' the old woman said _____ .

2 Tick the correct pictures. Then read *The Mad Hatter's Tea Party* on pages 52–53 of your Pupils' Book.

1

a

b ✔

2

a

b

3

a

b

4

a

b

3 Read and tick the correct sentences.

1 a The Mad Hatter, the March Hare and the mouse want Alice to sit at the table. _____

b The Mad Hatter, the March Hare and the mouse don't want Alice to sit at the table. ✔

2 a The mouse doesn't talk to Alice. _____

b The mouse talks a lot. _____

3 a Alice doesn't think the Mad Hatter and the March Hare are very polite. _____

b Alice thinks the Mad Hatter and the March Hare are very polite. _____

4 a Alice cuts her hair. _____

b Alice doesn't cut her hair. _____

5 a The Mad Hatter has a watch with numbers. _____

b The Mad Hatter has a watch with the days of the week. _____

6 a The March Hare puts the watch in his tea. _____

b The March Hare puts the watch in his cake. _____

4 Read and write True or False.

1 There was a small table under the tree. _____False_____

2 The Mad Hatter invited Alice to tea. _____

3 They drank wine. _____

4 The March Hare put butter on the watch. _____

5 The Mad Hatter thinks his watch is strange. _____

6 Alice thinks the watch is strange. _____

5 Match the sentences with the same meaning.

1 There isn't a place for you.

2 We didn't invite you to tea.

3 That wasn't very polite of you.

4 The Mad Hatter opened his eyes very wide.

a You didn't speak nicely.

b He was very surprised.

c We didn't ask you to come.

d There aren't any seats for you to sit on.

1 **Choose and write.**

Oscar   carriage   ribbon   ~~voice~~   accidentally   door   hopped

Jack and Kelly were on the train. Kelly heard a (1) _____voice_____ . It was Claudia. Claudia and

Magnus had (2) _____ . Magnus tried to tie a (3) _____ around Oscar but Oscar

ran into the next (4) _____ . The children hid behind the (5) _____ . Magnus stood

on Claudia. She (6) _____ up and down and then she (7) _____ hit Magnus.

2 **Circle the words that are body parts. Then label the picture.**

elbow

carriages

hit

hiding

ribbon

hop

tummy

(neck)

toes

fingers

around

knees

1 _____neck_____

2 _____

3 _____

4 _____

5 _____

6 _____

3 **Write the words you didn't circle in 2.**

1 Can you _____hop_____ on one leg?

2 She put a pink _____ in her hair.

3 The road went _____ the castle.

4 The train had six _____ .

5 They're _____ behind the door.

6 She _____ the tennis ball very hard.

4 **Look and write. Then circle True or False.**

1 _____Claudia's_____ voice is loud.
(True) / False

2 _____ nose is long.
True / False

3 _____ face is friendly.
True / False

4 _____ hair is short.
True / False

5 _____ tummy is big.
True / False

6 _____ feathers are green. True / False

5 **Look and write.**

Liam   Anita   Carl   Hannah

1 _____It's Hannah's_____ ribbon.
2 _____They're Liam's_____ binoculars.
3 _____ mobile phone.

4 _____ water pistol.
5 _____ rollerblades.
6 _____ map.

6 **Look at 5. Circle and answer.**

1 Whose money (is it) / are they?   _____It's Carl's money._____
2 Whose torch is it / are they?   _____
3 Whose sunglasses is it / are they?   _____
4 Whose watch is it / are they?   _____
5 Whose books is it / are they?   _____
6 Whose photos is it / are they?   _____

5b Is it yours?

1 Read and correct one word.

1 Oscar is Kelly and Jack's ~~cats~~. _____cat_____

2 Claudia and Magnus gets off the train. _____

3 Kelly finding a glove. _____

4 Kelly see Magnus's bag. _____

5 There is some clothes in the bag. _____

6 They doesn't rescue Toto. _____

2 Look, choose and write. Then answer.

scarf   belt   ~~gloves~~   trainers   jacket   ~~tie~~

Sue

Kevin

1 Whose _____gloves_____ are they?
   They're Sue's.

2 Whose _____tie_____ is it?
   It's Kevin's.

3 Whose _____ is it?
   _____

4 Whose _____ is it?
   _____

5 Whose _____ are they?
   _____

6 Whose _____ is it?
   _____

3 Tick and cross for you. Then write.

What clothes have you got?

I've got _____ .

I haven't got _____ .

4 **Rewrite the sentences. Use mine, yours, his, hers, ours, theirs.**

1 Is this your bag? _____Is this yours?_____

2 No, but that's my camera.

_____

3 They're our shoes. _____

4 That's her mobile. _____

5 We can't find his ticket. _____

6 Have you got their laptop?

_____

5 **Choose and write.**

mine   glasses   are   his   ~~is~~   hers   Whose   yours

Mum: Look at this mess. Whose belt (1) _____is_____ this? Is it (2) _____ , David?

David: No, it isn't (3) _____ . It's Sarah's.

Mum: What about these (4) _____ ?

David: They're (5) _____ , too.

Mum: These trainers look like Ivan's.

David: Yes, I think they're (6) _____ .

Mum: (7) _____ gloves are these?

David: They (8) _____ yours, Mum!

6 **Look and write questions. Then match and write answers. Use mine, his, hers, ours, theirs.**

1 _____Whose dog is it?_____

2 _____

3 _____

4 _____

5 _____

a _____

b _____

c It's ours.

d _____

e _____

55

You don't have to shout!

1 Listen and number the pictures in order. •))

1

2 Match the opposites. Then choose and write.

1	leave	**a**	find
2	start	**b**	arrive
3	bring	**c**	take
4	lose	**d**	finish

1 The children ___leave___ home at five past eight and ___arrive___ at school at quarter to nine.

2 The lessons _____ at nine o'clock and _____ at three.

3 My brothers sometimes _____ their football in the house but my mum tells them to _____ it outside.

4 In class they sometimes _____ their pencils but they always _____ some more.

3 Read and circle.

Yesterday I (1) (went) / looked to London with my family. The trip (2) landed / started well. We (3) left / needed home early and (4) arrived / asked there about ten o'clock. We (5) helped / visited the Tower of London. Then we (6) stopped / had a picnic lunch in a nice park.

After lunch there was a disaster! My mum (7) lost / came her bag with her money and mobile phone. We went to the police station and (8) met / dropped a man at the front door. He (9) had / made my mum's bag! He said he (10) found / wanted it under a seat in the park!

My mum was very happy. She (11) stayed / took us to a café and we had a wonderful dinner before we came home. The day (12) brought / finished happily.

4 Choose and write. Use **have to** or **has to**.

run   pack   ~~learn~~   buy   walk   throw   listen   invite

1 We want to speak English well.
____You have to learn____ the new words.
_____ to your teacher.

2 He wants to play basketball.
_____ fast.
_____ the ball well.

3 She wants to have a picnic.
_____ some friends.
_____ some food.

4 They want to stay with their grandma.
_____ their bags.
_____ to their grandma's house.

5 Look and write questions and answers.

1 be on a lead?   ____Does it have to be on a lead?____   ____Yes, it does.____
2 walk with their bikes?   ____Do they____   ____No,____
3 put the litter in the bin?   _____   _____
4 listen to the radio quietly?   _____   _____
5 walk with his rollerblades?   _____   _____

6 Write about you. Use **have to/don't have to**.

1 ____I have to____ do my homework.
2 _____ learn Maths.
3 _____ wear black shoes at school.
4 _____ arrive at school on time.
5 _____ learn a musical instrument.
6 _____ go to school on Saturday.

5d
SKILLS

I arrive at twenty to nine.

Look!

It's ten *past* eight.   It's quarter *to* nine.

Writing class: writing the time ✏

1 **Look and match.**

① ② ③ ④

a It's five past six.   **b** It's quarter past twelve.   **c** It's ten to four.   **d** It's twenty-five to three.

---

2 **Look, circle and write.**

1 We have an English lesson at ⊙ quarter / (twenty) to _____eleven_____ .

2 We go to the playground at ⊙ five / ten past _____ .

3 I arrive home at ⊙ twenty / twenty-five past _____ .

4 I do my homework at ⊙ quarter / ten to _____ .

---

3 **Number the sentences in order.**

a School finishes at twenty past three.   _____
b We have lunch at ten past twelve.   _____
c Every day I leave home at half past eight.   _1_
d The afternoon lessons start at one o'clock.   _____

e The first lesson starts at five past nine.   _____
f After school I go to the swimming pool for my swimming lesson.   _____
g I arrive at school at quarter to nine.   _____

---

4 **What about you?** **Write about your school day.**

Write
• what time you leave home and arrive at school.
• what time you have lunch and what you eat.
• what time you finish school and what you do after school.

My school day

Every day I _____

_____

_____

5 Read and match. Then draw.

a I have to go to the music room now.
I've got a piano lesson.
It starts at twenty-five to three.

c I have to go to the swimming pool now.
I've got a swimming lesson.
It starts at quarter to six.

b I have to go to the playing field now.
I've got a football match.
It starts at half past five.

d I have to go to the school hall now.
I've got a dance lesson.
It starts at five past twelve

6 Match. Then write in the correct order to make a dialogue.

1 I have to go to the   **a** for?
2 At quarter   **b** it start?
3 What   **c** swimming lesson.
4 I've got a   **d** later.
5 OK. See you   **e** swimming pool now.
6 What time does   **f** to six.

A: I have to go to the swimming pool now.
B: _____
A: _____
B: _____
A: _____
B: _____

7 Choose and write.

ten past four   music room   trumpet lesson

1 (I have to _____)   (What for?)

2 (_____)   (What time does it start?)

3 (_____)   (OK. See you later.)

1 **Label the pictures.**

apron   dress   ~~cap~~   tunic   trainers

1 _cap_

2 _____

3 _____

4 _____

5 _____

21st century   18th century   14th century   12th century

2 **Look at 1 and write.**

1 21st century _____ The cap is from the twenty-first century. _____

2 14th century _____

3 18th century _____

4 12th century _____

5 21st century _____

3 **Look at 1 and write.**

1 The boy lived in the _____twelfth_____ century. He wore _____a tunic, a belt, trousers and shoes_____ .

2 The man lived in the _____ century. He wore _____ .

3 The woman lived in the _____ century. She wore _____ .

4 The girl is living in the _____ century. She's wearing _____ .

4 Choose and write.

nurses ~~year~~ name shoes work uniform

Today the fashions change every (1) _____year_____ and people wear many different styles of clothes. You can choose the clothes you wear. However some people have to wear special clothes when they go to (2) _____ . They have to wear a
(3) _____ . Firefighters, police officers and
(4) _____ all wear uniforms at work. In Britain many children also have to wear uniforms when they go to school. At most primary schools the children wear a special sweater with the school (5) _____ and logo on it, with a dark skirt or trousers. At secondary school the children have to wear a school tie and a jacket called a 'blazer' with a skirt or trousers and brown or black (6) _____ . They also have special clothes for PE with a shirt, shorts and socks in the school colours.

5 Look at 4, read and answer.

1 Which jobs have uniforms?   _firefighters, police officers and nurses_

2 Do all children in Britain wear school uniforms? _____

3 What does a primary school child's sweater have on it? _____

4 Who wears a school tie?   _____

5 What is a 'blazer'?   _____

6 What is special about the clothes for PE?   _____

6 Your project! Answer about you.
Then draw your favourite clothes.

1 What clothes do you wear to school?

_____

2 What do you wear when you play sport?

_____

3 What do you wear at the beach?

_____

4 What do you wear in winter?

_____

5 What are your favourite clothes?

_____

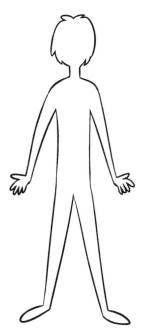

6a The red van is better!

1 Match.

1 What colour is Dr Wild's van?
2 Where are Claudia and Magnus?
3 Where are they going?
4 Are there three helicopters?
5 Does Dr Wild know how to fly a helicopter?

a No, there are two.
b on a motorbike
c It's red.
d Yes, she does.
e to the airport

2 Label the picture.

motorbike   ~~fire engine~~   van   scooter   helicopter

1 fire engine

3 Read and write words from 2.

1 It's got two wheels and can go very fast: ___motorbike___ .

2 Firemen drive it: _____ .

3 It flies in the air: _____ .

4 It's got two wheels and doesn't go very fast: _____ .

5 It's bigger than a car and has four wheels: _____ .

4 Read and write True or False.

1 Helicopters are bigger than cars. __True__
2 Cars are slower than bikes. _____
3 Motorbikes are faster than bikes. _____

4 Ambulances are smaller than scooters. _____
5 Scooters are smaller than vans. _____
6 Fire engines are bigger than motorbikes. _____

5 Look and write.

This is my family. Mum is much (1) ____shorter____ (short) than Dad. My brother Simon is 13 but he's

(2) _____ (tall) than my mum. Simon is (3) _____ (old) than my sister Bella. She's five

and she's (4) _____ (young) than me. Bella is (5) _____ (happy) than Simon because

she's got a (6) _____ (big) ball! Simon and Dad love playing football but Simon's clothes are

always (7) _____ (dirty) than Dad's.

6 Answer about you. Write full sentences.

1 Are you older than your teacher? _____No, I'm younger than my teacher._____
2 Are you taller than your dad? _____
3 Is your school smaller than your house? _____
4 Is your nose bigger than an elephant's? _____
5 Are your feet smaller than a cat's? _____
6 Is a giraffe shorter than you? _____

1 Listen and tick the correct pictures.

2 Look at 1, choose and write.

runner   light   ~~catch~~   noisy   silly

1 The children can't _____catch_____ the dog.

2 The chair is plastic and it's _____ .

3 It's very _____ where the children are.

4 Damian is _____ but he's a very fast _____ .

3 Read and write words from 2.

1 My little sister is only one and she can't _____catch_____ a ball.

2 'Be quiet!' said the teacher. 'Don't be _____ .'

3 Feathers aren't heavy. They're_____ .

4 I like the clowns at the circus. They're funny and _____ , too.

5 My friend is good at sport. He's a very fast _____ .

4 Look and answer.

Matt   Carol   David

1 Is David the shortest? _____Yes, he is._____   **4** Is David the fastest runner? _____

2 Is Carol the tallest? _____   **5** Has Carol got the shortest hair? _____

3 Is Carol faster than David? _____   **6** Has Matt got the longest hair? _____

5 Look and write.

Ben   Betsy   Tony   Katya   Ron   Poppy

1 strong _____Ron is the strongest child._____   **4** tall _____

2 silly _____   **5** long/hair _____

3 short _____   **6** short/hair _____

6 Write about people in your class.

1 tall/girl _____The tallest girl is_____   **4** fast/runner _____

2 short/girl _____   **5** funny/child _____

3 tall/boy _____   **6** strong/child _____

Oscar has got the softest bed!

1 **Choose and write.**

people ~~Ukraine~~ fun their staying there computer tobogganing different

Jack, Kelly and Dr Wild are in
(1) _____Ukraine_____ now. They're
(2) _____ at the Hotel Trendy and Claudia
and Magnus are in a (3) _____ hotel.
Jack likes (4) _____ hotel because
(5) _____ 's a (6) _____ in every
room. Kelly can see (7) _____ skiing and
having (8) _____ . Jack wants to go
(9) _____ .

2 **Choose and write.**

rich cheap dark soft ~~hard~~ easy

1 The chairs at my school are wooden and they're very _____hard_____ .

2 That jacket is only 5 euros. It's really _____ .

3 My uncle's got lots of money. He's very _____ .

4 Can you put the light on, please? It's _____ in here.

5 My baby sister's hair is so _____ .

6 Look at this question, 'What colour are bananas?' That's really _____ !

3 **Complete.**

soft	softer	the softest
hard	harder	
		the darkest
easy		
	worse	
good		
	cheaper	
		the richest
	sillier	
		the noisiest

4 **Look and answer.**

2+12=?   2845+346=?   2+2=?

Barry   Sam   David

1 Who is richer, David or Sam? _____Sam_____

2 Who is the richest? _____

3 Who is asking the easiest question?
_____

4 Who has got the lightest hair? _____

5 Who is sitting on the hardest chair?
_____

6 Whose chair is softer, Barry's or David's?
_____

5 **Look at 4, choose and write the correct form.**

~~rich~~   dark   easy   hard   dark   soft

1 Barry is _____richer_____ than David.

2 Sam's hair is _____ than Barry's.

3 Barry's question is _____ than Sam's.

4 Barry's chair is _____ than Sam's.

5 Sam's chair is the _____ .

6 David's hair is the _____ .

6 **Answer about you. Write full sentences.**

1 What's the best lesson at school?   _English is the best lesson at school._

2 Whose writing is better, yours or your friend's? _____

3 Which lesson is easier, Maths or English? _____

4 Where's the softest chair in your house? _____

5 Who has got the darkest hair in your family? _____

6 Which days are darker, winter days or summer days? _____

6d
SKILLS

Which bike do you like best?

Writing class: order of adjectives 🖊

1 **Choose and complete.**

~~grey~~   ~~amazing~~   ~~long~~   purple   cheap   orange   small
beautiful   white   great   short   funny   pretty   big
tall   black   high   yellow

Look!

opinion   size   colour
↓   ↓   ↓
It's got a *nice   small   blue* saddle.

Opinion	Size	Colour
_____	_____	_____
_____	_____	_____
_____	_____	_____
_____	_____	_____
_____	_____	_____
_____	_____	_____

2 **Write words from 1 in the correct order.**

1 He's got an _____*amazing*_____ _____ _____ car.

2 I saw a _____ _____ _____ bird yesterday.

3 It's a _____ _____ _____ bike.

3 **What about you?** Write an advertisement.

- Choose a name.
- Write about your opinion, the size and colour of the bike.
- Compare it to the other bikes in the shop.
- Is it the biggest, the fastest or the cheapest bike?

The _____ is a fantastic bike!
It's _____
_____
_____
_____
_____
_____

4 Look and tick.

Green Dragon €45　　　Sunshine €28　　　Rainbow Star €60

	Green Dragon	Sunshine	Rainbow Star
cheapest		✓	
biggest			
smallest			
longest tail			
shortest tail			
strongest			

5 Choose and write.

cheapest　sure　one　biggest　best　longest　~~favourite~~

Which is your (1) __favourite__ kite?

I'm not (2) _____ . Sunshine is the
(3) _____ but Rainbow Star is the
(4) _____ .

Green Dragon has got the (5) _____ tail.

So, which (6) _____ do you like (7) _____ ?

I like Rainbow Star!

6 Look at 4. Choose your favourite kite and write.

I like the _____ kite best.

It's the/It's got the _____ .

Science

1 Choose and write.

stars   furthest   rock   ~~gas~~   rings   ice

1 Some planets are made of _____gas_____ but Earth is made of _____ .

2 There are circles around some planets. The circles are called _____ .

3 When water is very cold, it's _____ .

4 Pluto isn't near the sun. It's the _____ from the sun.

5 At night you can see lots of _____ in the sky.

2 Put the letters in order and write.

1 uSn   _____Sun_____

2 crurMye   _____

3 snVeu   _____

4 tEhra   _____

5 rasM   _____

6 rpuitJe   _____

7 aSturn   _____

8 snrauU   _____

9 epuNten   _____

10 tlPou   _____

3 Write.

1 hot   Venus   _____is the hottest planet_____ .

2 big   Jupiter   _____ .

3 cold   Pluto   _____ .

4 near   Mercury   _____ to the sun.

5 far   Pluto   _____ from the sun.

6 small Pluto   _____ .

4 **Read and answer.**

The moon isn't a planet. It goes around our planet, Earth. It's made of rock. There are seas on the moon but there isn't any water in the seas.

There isn't any weather on the moon. It isn't windy there and it never snows or rains.

The moon is smaller than Earth. Sometimes it looks big; sometimes it looks small. When it's big and round, it's called a full moon. When it's very small, it's called a new moon.

The first men on the moon were Neil Armstrong and Edwin Aldrin. They landed on the moon on July 20th 1969 and they walked around for two hours.

1 What's the moon made of? _It's made of rock._

2 Can you swim in the seas on the moon? _____

3 Does it rain on the moon? _____

4 Which moon looks the biggest, a full moon or a new moon? _____

5 Do Neil Armstrong and Edwin Aldrin live on the moon? _____

5 **Your project!** **Look and write.**

	Mercury	Mars	Saturn	Uranus
Made of	rock	rock	gas	gas
Temperature	hot	cold	cold	cold
Other information	It looks like the moon.	It's red.	It's got rings of ice.	It's got five big moons.

(1) _____Uranus_____ has got five big (2) _____. It's made of gas and it's (3) _____.

(4) _____ is a red planet. It's (5) _____ and it's made of rock.

(6) _____ looks like the moon. It's (7) _____ and it's made of (8) _____.

(9) _____ is (10) _____ and it's made of (11) _____. It's got rings of (12) _____.

Review 3

1 Do the crossword. Then complete the sentence with the secret word.

1 You wear this on your head.

2 You wear this around your neck to keep you warm.

3 You wear this like a coat.

4 You can only wear this with a shirt.

5 You wear this when you cook.

6 You wear this to hold your trousers up.

7 Girls wear this.

8 You wear these on your hands.

1 h a t

2

3 c

4

5 p

6

7 s

8 o

You can't wear _____ to my school.

2 Match. Then write questions and answers.

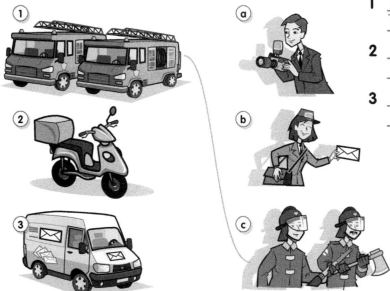

1 <u>Whose fire engines are they?</u>
<u>They're theirs.</u>

2 _____
_____

3 _____
_____

3 Write and say.

I (1) wa_l_ked for an (2) ___our last (3) We___nesday
(4) ni___ht on an (5) i___land. It was (6) autum___
and I (7) clim___ed up to a (8) cas___le!

4 Look and write.

1 old   _Clara is older than Mara. Tara is the oldest._____

2 young   _____

3 tall   _____

4 long/hair   _Clara's hair is_____

5 heavy/bag   _____

5 Choose and write questions and answers about your English lessons.

~~learn~~   work   sing   listen to   songs   ~~new words~~   your teacher   hard

1 _____ _Do you have to learn new words?_ _____ _____ _Yes, we do._ _____

2 _____   _____

3 _____   _____

4 _____   _____

My English

6 Look and write. Then check and answer.

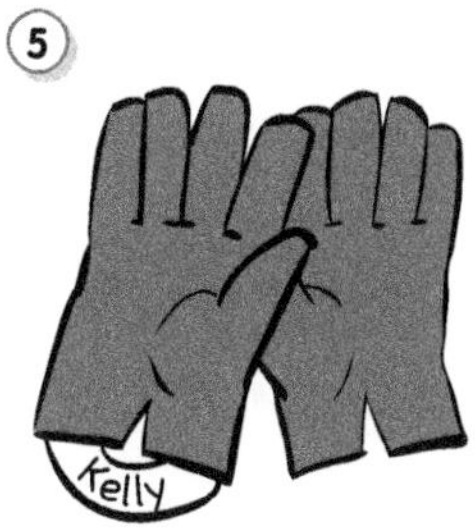

1 His _____ are dirty. ☐

2 The black dog is _____ than the white one. ☐

3 What's the time? It's _____ ☐ _____ seven.

4 There's a _____ behind ☐ the motorbike.

5 _____ gloves are these? ☐ They're _____ .

How did you do? _____   **1** = OK   **2–3** = Good   **4–5** = Excellent

73

The Prince and the Pauper

1 **Put the letters in order and write.**

1 I haven't got any money or a place to live so I have to __beg__ (ebg) on the streets.

2 The _____ (doleris) wore a red jacket and black trousers and he looked after the palace.

3 A _____ (garbeg) asked me for some money this morning.

4 The rich man had a big house. Lots of _____ (venstars) worked there.

5 The _____ (pepura) had no money and his clothes were old and dirty.

6 We often give food to the _____ (opro) people in my town.

2 **Number the pictures in order. Then read _The Prince and the Pauper_ on pages 76–77 of your Pupils' Book.**

3 Look at 2, choose and write.

~~Tom was a pauper. He went to the palace every day.~~
The prince and Tom changed clothes.
A servant brought lots of good food for Tom to eat.
Tom saw Prince Edward in the palace. A soldier hit Tom!
The prince had an idea. He wanted to be a pauper and play with other boys.
The prince was angry with the soldier. He invited Tom into the palace.
The prince ran out of the palace. Tom didn't know what to do.
The prince and Tom talked. The prince liked Tom's stories.

Picture 1: _Tom was a pauper. He went to the palace every day._

Picture 2: _____

Picture 3: _____

Picture 4: _____

Picture 5: _____

Picture 6: _____

Picture 7: _____

Picture 8: _____

4 Read and write True or False.

1 Tom's home was the palace.   _____False_____

2 Tom's family was rich.   _____

3 Tom sometimes asked other people for money.   _____

4 Prince Edward kicked Tom.   _____

5 The prince had lots of friends.   _____

6 The prince wanted to be a poor boy for a day.   _____

5 Choose and write.

poor   day   ~~lived~~   sisters   servants   room   food   rich   palace   boys

Tom (1) ___lived___ with his (2) _____ , his parents and his grandmother in one (3) _____ .
They were very (4) _____ and they were always hungry. Prince Edward lived in a (5) _____ with
his father, the king, and lots of (6) _____ . They were very (7) _____ and they always had lots of
(8) _____ . Tom had friends and he played with them. The prince didn't have any friends. There
weren't any other (9) _____ in the palace. The prince wanted to live like Tom for a
(10) _____ .

1 Match.

1 Where are Jack, Kelly and Dr Wild?	a She likes the pop star costume.
2 What are the other people wearing?	b Claudia
3 Does Dr Wild say Kelly and Jack can join in?	c He's tobogganing.
4 Which costume does Kelly like?	d Yes, she does.
5 Which costume does Jack like?	e in the mountains
6 What's Oscar doing?	f fancy dress
7 Who's pulling the toboggan?	g He likes the superhero costume.

2 Look, choose and write.

costumes   join in   alien   spy   superhero   ~~fancy dress~~   pop star

1 ___fancy dress___

NEW (2) _____

COME AND (3) _____

_____ THE FUN!

4 _____   5 _____   6 _____   7 _____

3 Read and write words from 2.

1 He's wearing a raincoat and a false beard and moustache. Do you think he's a _____spy_____ ?

2 I'm reading a book about an _____ . He comes from the planet Jupiter.

3 We're in the school play. Our mum has to make our _____ .

4 I like Batman. Who's your favourite _____ ?

5 Let's go to a concert. My favourite _____ is singing at the town hall.

6 I'm going to a _____ party tonight.

7 I'm playing football with my friends. Do you want to _____ ?

4 Look, choose and write.

~~ride~~ fly chase go play make

1	_She wants to ride_ her bike.	**4**	_____ a sandcastle.
2	_____ on the swing.	**5**	_____ tennis.
3	_____ a kite.	**6**	_____ the cat.

5 Look and write.

1 play _He wants to play basketball._

2 go _They don't_ _____

3 make _____

4 climb _____

5 carry _____

6 Answer about you.

1 What do you want to do after school today? _____

2 What do you want to eat for dinner? _____

3 What do you want to do next weekend? _____

4 Where do you want to go next holiday? _____

1 Listen and circle. 🔊

2 Circle the words that are activities.

evening   (fishing)   cycling   swing   rock climbing   skateboarding   morning

climbing frame   surfing   lightning   wing   ice skating

3 Look at 1 and write activities from 2.

1 He wants to go _____fishing_____ .

2 They want to go _____ .

3 They want to go _____ .

4 She wants to go _____ .

5 He wants to go _____ .

6 They want to go _____ .

4 Look and write.

1 like   <u>He doesn't like running.</u>

2 good at   <u>She's good at jumping.</u>

3 enjoy   _____

4 good at   _____

5 good at   _____

6 enjoy   _____

7 like   _____

8 good at   _____

5 Correct the sentences.

1 I happy when I'm cycling.   <u>I'm happy when I'm cycling.</u>

2 I'm good at skateboard.   _____

3 He's happy when he fishing.   _____

4 She don't like rock climbing.   _____

5 They're good in ice skating.   _____

6 Do you enjoy play volleyball?   _____

6 Write about you.

1 I like (+ something you do with your friends) _____ .

2 I'm good at (+ something you do in the playground) _____ .

3 I don't like (+ something you do every day) _____ .

4 I'm not good at (+ a sport) _____ .

5 I'm happy when I'm (+ something you do at home) _____ .

6 I enjoy (+ something you do at school) _____ .

1 Tick the correct sentences.

1 a Magnus was a teacher and Claudia was a doctor. _____

  b Magnus was an alien and Claudia was a spy. ✔

2 a Claudia and Magnus are halfway down the mountain. _____

  b Claudia and Magnus are halfway down the hotel. _____

3 a There isn't time to use the helicopter. _____

  b There isn't time to make a helicopter. _____

4 a Dr Wild isn't very good at speaking. _____

  b Dr Wild isn't very good at skiing. _____

5 a A man helps them. _____

  b A man hits them. _____

6 a They borrow a toboggan. _____

  b They borrow a can opener. _____

2 Circle the odd one out.

1 alien   pop star   (rescue)   superhero

2 borrow   sun   star   moon

3 tie   belt   scarf   escaped

4 niece   hold   nephew   uncle

5 silly   using   funny   noisy

6 behind   along   reach   across

3 Write sentences using the circled words in 2. Then match.

1 Let's/the cat. __Let's rescue the cat._____

2 They need to/a torch. _____

3 It was open so our dog/from the garden. _____

4 I can/the boat for you. _____

5 The children aren't/the spade. _____

6 They want to/the bridge before they stop for lunch. _____

4 **Write Shall we or What about. Then match.**

1 ___What about___ going to the toy shop?   **a** OK. I've got my bike.

2 _____ take a picnic?   **b** I don't want to. I haven't got any money.

3 _____ go cycling?   **c** No, thanks. I don't want to get wet.

4 _____ making a cake?   **d** OK. Do you want to count or hide?

5 _____ having a water fight?   **e** OK. We need to buy some flour.

6 _____ play Hide and Seek?   **f** Good idea. I can make some sandwiches.

5 **Match and write.**

1
| watching a different film |
| come back tomorrow |

a (Oh, no! It's raining.)

Shall we _____ ?

What about _____ ?

2
| jump across |
| finding a bridge |

b (Oh, no! We're late. The film started ten minutes ago.)

Shall we ___come back tomorrow___ ?

What about _____ ?

3
| go home |
| standing under the slide |

c (Oh, no! A stream! What shall we do?)

Shall we _____ ?

What about _____ ?

6 **Read and make suggestions. Use Shall we …? or What about …?**

1 You and your friend want to do something exciting.   _____

2 It's raining and you and your friend are at your house.   _____

3 An English girl is visiting you for the day.   _____

Writing class: using *or* in questions

Look!
Have you got any DVDs or computer games? Do you want to watch a film or play computer games?

1 **Look and write.**

1 Do you like ___toboganing or skiing___ ?

2 Do you want to go _____ ?

3 Shall we go _____ ?

4 What about _____ ?

5 Shall we play _____ ?

2 **Write suggestions.**

1 meet/in town/in the park? ___Do you want to meet in town or in the park?___

2 play tennis/football/in the morning? _____

3 have lunch/at my house/in a café? _____

4 go to the museum/the cinema/in the afternoon? _____

5 watch TV/play on the computer/in the evening? _____

3 **What about you?** **Write an email making suggestions for Saturday.**

- Write suggestions about where to meet.

- Write two suggestions about what to do in the morning, for lunch, in the afternoon, in the evening.

Hi _____

I'm very happy that you're free on Saturday. _____

_____

_____

See you soon.

_____

4 Number the dialogue in order.

Danny

Elaine

a I don't want to go surfing today. ☐

b OK. Let's go. ☐

c I don't know. Have you got any ideas? ☐

d Yes, rock climbing is a great idea. ☐

e What about surfing? ☐

f Do you like rock climbing? ☐

g What shall we do this morning? ☐ 1

5 Choose and write.

want   know   ~~shall we~~   great idea   Do   What about

Elaine: What (1) __shall we__ do this afternoon, Danny?

Danny: I don't (2) _____ . Have you got any ideas?

Elaine: (3) _____ swimming?

Danny: I don't (4) _____ to go swimming today.

Elaine: (5) _____ you like fishing?

Danny: Yes, fishing is a (6) _____ .

Elaine: OK. Let's go.

6 Look at 4 and 5 and write.

1 Elaine doesn't want to go ___surfing___ in the morning.

2 She wants to go _____ .

3 Danny doesn't want to go _____ in the afternoon.

4 He wants to go _____ .

1 Match and write.

1 Olympic   a medal   1 _Olympic flag_
2 world   b a goal   2 _____
3 football   c flag   3 _____
4 gold   d player   4 _____
5 score   e record   5 _____

2 Look and complete.

	Verb	Person
1 	play tennis	
2 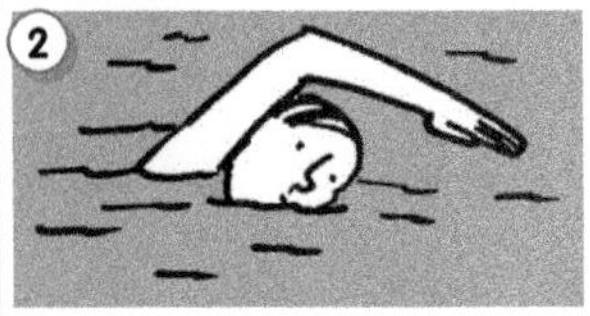		
3 		
4 		
5 		

3 Circle.

1 How fast can you (run) / running?

2 He's an amazing tennis / tennis player.

3 I play football / football every weekend.

4 The team playing basket / play basketball really well.

5 Do you think she's a good swimmer / swimming?

4 Choose and write.

won   competed   records   ~~sportswoman~~   used   gold   Olympic   swimming

wheelchair

Tanni Grey-Thompson can't walk but she's an amazing
(1) <u>sportswoman</u> . She was born in Wales in 1969 and first
(2) _____ a wheelchair when she was seven years old.
She was good at sports and she enjoyed (3) _____ and
horse riding. She started wheelchair racing when she was 13 and
six years later she (4) _____ in the 1988 Seoul Paralympic
Games, the (5) _____ Games for people who can't walk
or see well. She's got 11 (6) _____ medals, which she
(7) _____ in five Paralympic Games. She broke the world
(8) _____ for the 100-metre, 400-metre and 800-metre
wheelchair races. She also won the London Wheelchair Marathon
six times.

5 Look at 4, read and write True or False.

1 Tanni Grey-Thompson is from Wales. __True__

2 She started using a wheelchair in 1979. _____

3 She was good at playing the drums. _____

4 She enjoyed cycling. _____

5 She won medals in five Paralympic Games. _____

6 She's got 11 gold medals. _____

7 She won the New York Marathon six times. _____

6 Your project! Look and write.

Sport	tennis
Favourite player	Serena Williams
Nationality	American
Date of birth	26.9.1981
Achievements	27 Grand Slam titles 2 Olympic gold medals

I like (1) __playing tennis__ .
I like watching it, too. There are lots of
great players but my favourite is
(2) _____ . She's from the
(3) _____ and she was born
in September, (4) _____ .
She started playing tennis when she was
four years old. Today she's one of the best
tennis players in the world and she's got
(5) _____ titles. She's also
got two (6) _____ .
One day I want to be a famous tennis player
like Serena.

8a I'm going to phone the police!

1 Choose and write.

hiding   police   sofa   knocked over   under   upstairs   ~~hotel~~   prison   holding

Dr Wild, Jack and Kelly see Claudia and Magnus go into a (1) _____hotel_____ . Claudia is

(2) _____ Oscar. Jack looks (3) _____ for Claudia and Magnus. They

(4) _____ a lamp in a bedroom so Jack and Kelly know they're (5) _____ there.

Toto is hiding on the (6) _____ and Oscar is (7) _____ the rug. The (8) _____

arrive and take Claudia and Magnus to (9) _____ .

2 Find and circle five items from a living room. Then write.

1 ____cushion____

2 _____

3 _____

4 _____

5 _____

c	u	r	t	a	i	n
u	w	u	y	i	k	o
s	v	g	b	s	e	r
h	x	c	l	a	m	p
i	s	x	e	z	a	j
o	i	p	w	e	e	a
n	s	o	f	a	g	t

3 Look and write about Jack's and Kelly's bedrooms.

Jack's bedroom

Kelly's bedroom

Jack has got a bed and (1) ____a rug____ next
to the bed. He's got (2) _____ and
(3) _____ . There's (4) _____ on the
desk. He's got short (5) _____ . He hasn't got
a sofa.

Kelly has got a bed but she hasn't got
(1) _____ . She's got (2) _____ . There
are two (3) _____ on (4) _____ .
She's got long (5) _____ . She hasn't got
(6) _____ or (7) _____ .

4 Match and circle.

1 There are lots of black clouds in the sky.
2 It's my mum's birthday tomorrow.
3 The sofa is very hard.
4 My sisters are hungry.
5 My curtains are very old.

a They're going to have some stew / a shower.
b It's going to (rain) / snow.
c I'm going to buy some new ones / an old one.
d She's going to have a party / some water.
e We're going to get some more cushions / lamps.

5 Choose and write. Use going to.

take   go   hide   ~~phone~~   catch

Look at that man and woman. They're thieves!

1 I _'m going to phone_ the police.

2 The dog _____ behind the tree.

3 He _____ the money.

4 The police _____ them!

5 They _____ _____ to prison!

1 **Listen and tick the party the boy went to. Then read and write** True **or** False.

1 He went to a fancy dress party.
_____True_____

2 It was a Welcome Home party.
_____

3 Sarah sent invitations with stars on them.
_____

4 They ate sandwiches, a cake and oranges.
_____

2 **Do the crossword.**

1 You can wear this to a party.

2 This is when you take food to eat outside.

3 It's a good idea to do this before you do something new.

4 To play or do things with other people. (2 words)

5 This is a long flag.

6 You give these to your friends before a party.

7 To put a letter in the post.

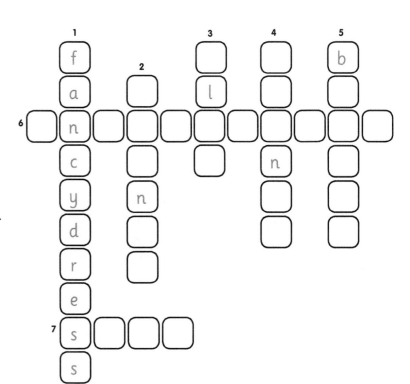

3 Look and write questions and answers.

1 they/have/a picnic? ✓
2 they/go to school? ✗
3 the dog/swim in the river? ✓
4 she/climb a tree? ✓
5 he/play tennis? ✗

1 ___Are they going to have a picnic?___ ___Yes, they are.___
2 _____ _____
3 _____ _____
4 _____ _____
5 _____ _____

4 Write sentences.

1 She/go to the shops. ✗   beach ✓
___She isn't going to go to the shops.___
___She's going to go to the beach.___

2 They/make a cake. ✗   some invitations ✓
_____
_____

3 He/play the guitar. ✗   the drums ✓
_____
_____

4 They/tidy the living room. ✗   their bedroom ✓
_____
_____

5 My sister/play basketball. ✗   football ✓
_____
_____

6 My brother/paint the walls. ✗ a banner ✓
_____
_____

5 Tick and cross for this weekend. Then write about you.

1 do my homework _____   3 go swimming _____   5 tidy my bedroom _____
2 have a picnic _____   4 have a dance lesson _____ 6 play computer games _____

1 ___I'm going to do my homework./I'm not going to do my homework.___
2 _____
3 _____
4 _____
5 _____
6 _____

Why did they want Toto?

1 **Look, read and correct one word.**

1 The policewoman is talking to ~~Kelly~~. ___Dr Wild___   **4** They're sitting on rugs. _____

2 Jack is giving Toto a biscuit. _____   **5** There are four cushions. _____

3 Kelly is looking for Oscar. _____

2 **Look at 1. Read and circle the person who is thinking each thing.**

1 'I love sitting with Kelly.'   Jack / (Oscar) / Toto

2 'We wanted these robbers for a long time.'   the policeman / Jack / Kelly

3 'I like bananas!'   Jack / Toto / Dr Wild

4 'They helped us with our job.'   Oscar / Kelly / the policewoman

3 **Choose and write.**

rare   Robbers   steal   jewellery   ~~valuable~~   paintings   Diamonds

1 You need lots of money to buy a ___valuable___ thing.

2 _____ are hard stones.

3 You can see lots of famous _____ in art galleries.

4 When something is _____ , there aren't many of them in the world.

5 _____ are people who take things without asking for them.

6 It's wrong to _____ money.

7 You can wear _____ round your neck, on your ears and on your fingers.

4 Circle and write words from 3.

1 Claudia and Magnus are going to go to prison why / (because) they're ____robbers____ .

2 Why / Because did they _____ Toto? Why / Because Claudia likes _____ birds.

3 In their house in Switzerland the police found lots of _____ . Why / Because were they there? Claudia and Magnus took them from art galleries why / because they're _____ .

4 There was lots of beautiful _____ , too. Why / Because did Claudia steal it? Why / Because she loves _____ .

5 Match.

1 Why are you going to the shops?   a Because I like swimming.

2 Why are you going to the bank?   b Because I want to read some books.

3 Why are you going to the pool?   c Because I've got stomachache.

4 Why are you going to the library?   d Because I need some money.

5 Why are you going to the art gallery?   e Because I want to see some famous paintings.

6 Why aren't you eating your dinner?   f Because I want to buy some new clothes.

6 Choose and write.

my teachers are funny   they're funny   I can go to the beach   I can go tobogganing

we learn interesting things   we play games together   ~~it's warm and sunny~~   there's lots of snow

1 I like summer because …

a ____it's warm and sunny____ .   b _____ .

2 I like winter because …

a _____ .   b _____ .

3 I like school because …

a _____ .   b _____ .

4 I like my friends because …

a _____ .   b _____ .

7 Answer for you.

1 Why do you like summer?   _____

2 Why do you like winter?   _____

3 Why do you like your school?   _____

4 Why do you like your friends?   _____

8d SKILLS

Would you like to come to our party?

Writing class: writing dates

1 **Look and write the dates.**

 ①  ②  ③  ④

① It's January 1st. _____ _____ _____

2 **Write the months in order.**

June   April   ~~January~~   December   May   February
October   March   July   September   August   November

1 J anuary_____   5 M _____   9 S _____

2 F _____   6 J _____   10 O _____

3 M _____   7 J _____   11 N _____

4 A _____   8 A _____   12 D _____

3 **Match.**

1 third	**a** 1st		7 twenty-first	**g** 30th
2 first	**b** 2nd		8 twenty-second	**h** 28th
3 fifth	**c** 3rd		9 thirtieth	**i** 21st
4 second	**d** 4th		10 thirty-first	**j** 22nd
5 sixth	**e** 5th		11 twenty-eighth	**k** 20th
6 fourth	**f** 6th		12 twentieth	**l** 31st

4 **What about you?**

Write an invitation to a party.

- What kind of party is it?
- When is it going to be?
- Where are you going to have it?
- How do your guests reply to the invitation?

PLEASE COME TO MY PARTY!

The occasion: ....

The time: ....

The date: ....

The place: ....

RSVP Tel: ....   Email: ....

5 Match.

1 Would you like
2 I'd
3 What
4 It's on
5 It's at
6 See you
7 Where

a Friday.
b to come to my party?
c is it?
d my house.
e then.
f love to come.
g time is it?

6 Look at 5 and write.

(1) _Would you like to_ come to my party?

Thank you. Yes, (2) _____. When is it?

It's on Friday.

(3) _____

It's at seven o'clock.

(4) _____

It's at my house.

Great. (5) _____. Bye!

Bye!

7 Read and write.

Invitation!

It's Mel's birthday on Saturday May 27th and she's going to have a picnic at five o'clock in the park.

Mel: Would you (1) _like to come to my picnic_ ?

Beth: Thank you. Yes, I'd love to come. When (2) _____ ?

Mel: It's (3) _____.

Beth: What time is it?

Mel: It's (4) _____.

Beth: Where (5) _____ ?

Mel: It's (6) _____.

Beth: Great. See you then. Bye!

Mel: Bye!

Social Science

1 **Label the pictures.**

Award ~~Physical~~ Volunteering Expedition Skills

①  ②  ③  ④  ⑤

__Physical__ _____ _____ _____ _____

2 **Choose and write.**

sports help ~~Award~~ tent fourteen trip animals four learn computers

You can do the Duke of Edinburgh's (1) ____Award____ when you're (2) _____ or older. You
have to do something from (3) _____ sections. In the physical section you play
(4) _____ or games. In the volunteering section you (5) _____ other people or
(6) _____ . In the skills section you (7) _____ something new, like how to use
(8) _____ or play a musical instrument. Finally in the expedition section you go on a
(9) _____ with some friends and sleep in a (10) _____ for one night.

3 **Read and circle.**

1 You can do the awards when you're … years old.

    a 12   **b** 14   **c** 13

2 You can play football for the … section.

    a physical   **b** volunteering   **c** skills

3 You can learn to play the guitar for the … section.

    a physical   **b** volunteering   **c** skills

4 You sleep in a tent on the … .

    a award   **b** night   **c** expedition

4 **Read and complete.**

Hi, I'm Liam. I'm going to do the Bronze award. I'm going to help in an Old People's Home for the volunteering section because I know old people need lots of help. I'm going to take photos for the skills section. I'm going to do that because I've got a new camera and I want to learn to take good photos. I'm going to choose swimming for the physical section because I love swimming and I want to get better and faster. I'm going to go swimming three times a week and do a lifesaving course.

For the expedition I'm going to ride my bike along the River Thames because I like cycling. Four of my friends and a teacher are going to come with me. We have to carry the tents and equipment on our bikes. I'm really excited!

	Volunteering	Physical	Expedition	Skills
What is Liam going to do?	help in an Old People's Home			
Why?				

5 **Choose and complete.**

~~look after animals~~   cycle 50 miles   ice skate   walk up a mountain

paint   write a story   help children   play tennis

Volunteering	Physical	Expedition	Skills
look after animals			

6 **Your project!** **Write about you.**

For the expedition section I'd like to _____ because _____ .

For the volunteering section I'd like to _____ because _____ .

For the physical section I'd like to _____ because _____ .

For the skills section I'd like to _____ because _____ .

Review 4

1 **Look, choose and write.**

diamond	lamp	~~painting~~	tools	compass
jewellery	knock over	~~valuable~~	borrow	lost
buy	chasing	~~steal~~	escape	use

1 The robber is going to _____steal_____ the ___painting___ because it's ___valuable___ .

2 The woman is going to _____ the _____ because she likes _____ .

3 They're going to _____ the _____ because they're _____ .

4 The dog is going to _____ the _____ because it's _____ a cat.

5 The prisoner is going to _____ some _____ because he wants to _____

2 **Read, choose and write.**

eat a sandwich   open the window   drink some water   go to bed

~~escape from prison~~   hide behind the cushion

1 Claudia is unhappy.   _She wants to escape from prison._

2 Magnus is hungry.   _____

3 Toto is scared.   _____

4 Dr Wild is hot.   _____

5 Oscar is thirsty.   _____

6 Jack and Kelly are tired. _____

3 **Write th or t and say.**

(1) _Th_e (2) _____ree children were (3) _____irsty and
(4) _____ired and (5) _____ey (6) _____anked (7) _____eir
(8) _____eacher for (9) _____e (10) _____ea.

4 Circle.

1 I like sports and I'm good at ~~running~~ / climb / play football.

2 He's happy when he's ice skate / skiing / toboggan.

3 She wants jumping / to dive / swim in the swimming pool.

4 I've got a good idea. What about rollerblades / play basketball / cycling in the park?

5 Choose and write.

costume What about Shall Because be want to
going to ~~fancy dress~~ Why pop star

Ben: Wow! It's a carnival. Look at all the (1) __fancy dress__ costumes.

Kate: (2) _____ we join in?

Ben: Yes, I (3) _____ be a superhero. What are you

(4) _____ wear?

Kate: I don't know.

Ben: (5) _____ wearing this alien (6) _____ ?

Kate: No, I'm going to (7) _____ a pop star.

Ben: (8) _____ do you want to be a (9) _____ ?

Kate: (10) _____ I like these silver shoes.

My English

6 Look and write. Then check and answer.

1 He wants to _____ . ☐

2 It's _____ rain. ☐

3 She's good _____ climbing. ☐

4 She's got lots of _____ . ☐

5 What _____ we do today? ☐

What about _____ ?

How did you do? _____   **1** = OK   **2–3** = Good   **4–5** = Excellent

The Voyages of Sindbad the Sailor

1 **Read and circle.**

(1) Sailors / Teachers work on (2) schools / ships at sea. Their (3) captain / mother tells them what to do. They go away to sea for many weeks on long (4) cars / voyages. Sometimes the weather is bad and the sea is very (5) dangerous / sad. When it's stormy, the sailors are sometimes (6) afraid / happy of the sea. In the past ships were made of (7) colour / wood.

2 **Tick the correct pictures. Then read *The Voyages of Sindbad the Sailor* on pages 100–101 of your Pupils' Book.**

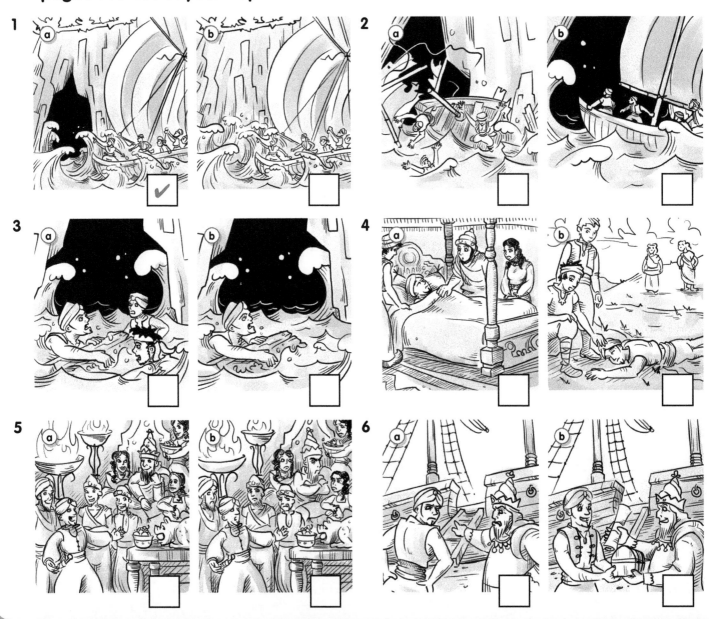

3 Read and circle.

1 The captain (didn't want) / wanted to go into the cave.

2 Sindbad helped / didn't help the other sailors in the cave.

3 Sindbad woke up next to a river / palace.

4 Sindbad knew the king of Serendip was dangerous / kind.

5 The king liked / didn't like Sindbad's stories.

6 Sindbad went / didn't go back to his home and his friends.

4 Read and write True or False.

1 Sindbad wanted to go on lots more voyages.   _____False_____

2 Sindbad climbed the mountain.   _____

3 Sindbad went by train to see the king of Serendip. _____

4 The king of Serendip was a good man.   _____

5 The King gave Sindbad a letter.   _____

6 It was stormy when Sindbad went home.   _____

5 Choose and write.

dangerous   stories   letter   afraid   ~~voyage~~   sailors   captain   ship

This was Sindbad's sixth (1) _____voyage_____ . The (2) _____ saw a big mountain. The
weather was very bad. He was (3) _____ . The (4) _____ went into a cave. It broke
and the other (5) _____ fell in the sea. It was very (6) _____ and the other men died.

Sindbad woke up and saw lots of people. He went to see the king of Serendip. The king was kind and
he liked listening to Sindbad's (7) _____ . He gave Sindbad a (8) _____ for his king
and many valuable things.

9a Oscar is enjoying the trip!

1 Read and circle.

Dr Wild and Kelly look for Jack but he (1) isn't / is in the hotel. He's with a man called Mr Falcon. Mr Falcon has got a hot air balloon they can (2) wash / use to travel home. They all (3) enjoy / hate flying in the hot air balloon and they (4) see / climb fields and a big forest. They're very (5) happy / scared when they get (6) home / up again and the children thank their (7) aunt / doctor for the great (8) picnic / adventure.

2 Choose and write.

~~return~~   hot air balloon   explain   disappear   trip

1 go or come back to a place: __return__

2 a visit somewhere for a few days: _____

3 a form of transport that carries people up into the sky: _____

4 make something clear: _____

5 go where you can't be seen: _____

3 Write words from 2 in the correct form. Then match.

1 We went on a school skiing ____trip____ last winter.   _c_

2 Our teacher _____ how to turn and fall.   _____

3 It got dark early. The sun _____ behind the mountains.   _____

4 We _____ to our hotel every day at four o'clock.   _____

5 On the last day we went up in a _____ . It was amazing! _____

4 Choose and write the correct form.

~~get up~~   work   go   get ready   cook   drive   get up   walk   be

My sister, Lizzy, always (1) _____gets up_____ at seven o'clock but I (2) _____ at quarter past seven. At the moment it's half past seven and we (3) _____ to go to school. My dad (4) _____ breakfast. My mum (5) _____ a doctor and she (6) _____ at the hospital in our town. She always (7) _____ to work very early. She (8) _____ to work in her car but we (9) _____ to school because it's very near our house.

5 Look and write was, wasn't, were or weren't.

It (1) _____wasn't_____ cloudy yesterday. It
(2) _____ sunny. My family and I
(3) _____ in a hot air balloon. My little
brother (4) _____ happy! He
(5) _____ scared but I (6) _____ .
I (7) _____ excited! Mum and Dad
(8) _____ nervous. They enjoyed flying.

There (9) _____ lots of trees and fields
all around us but there (10) _____ any
mountains.

It (11) _____ great fun and I
(12) _____ sad when we returned.

6 Tick and cross the activities you did/didn't do yesterday. Then write about you.

clean your teeth	✔	walk to school	_____	listen to music	_____
dance	_____	play a game	_____	phone a friend	_____
watch TV	_____	paint a picture	_____	use a computer	_____

I cleaned my teeth. I didn't _____

_____

_____

_____

_____

_____

I lost my paddle!

1 **Listen and tick the correct pictures.** •))

2 **Look at 1 and circle.**

1 The children are swimming / (canoeing.) The boy lost his paddle / boat.

2 The children are in a Chinese restaurant / at a picnic. They're eating sandwiches / soup.

3 The children are flying / horse riding. They don't want to go fast / slowly.

4 The children are horse riding / camping. They can hear / ride horses.

3 **Choose and write.**

horse riding   paddle   canoeing   Chinese   ~~restaurant~~   camping

1 This is a place to eat: _restaurant_ .

2 This word can go before *food, flag, girl, writing*: _____ .

3 You can do these activities on holiday: _____ , _____ , _____ .

4 You use this in the water to move a canoe: _____ .

4 **Look and write.**

1 go   They ____went____ to the UK.

They ___didn't go___ to the USA.

2 fly   He _____ in a plane.

He _____ in a helicopter.

3 sleep   She _____ in a castle.

She _____ in a hotel.

4 see   They _____ an owl.

They _____ a snake.

5 **Write questions. Then circle for you.**

1 go camping/last summer?

_____Did you go camping last summer?_____ Yes, I did. / No, I didn't.

2 send a letter/last week?

_____ Yes, I did. / No, I didn't.

3 climb a tree/yesterday?

_____ Yes, I did. / No, I didn't.

4 go horse riding/last weekend?

_____ Yes, I did. / No, I didn't.

5 go canoeing/last summer?

_____ Yes, I did. / No, I didn't.

6 eat Chinese food/last month?

_____ Yes, I did. / No, I didn't.

9c All our friends are going to be there.

1 Read and correct one word.

1 The picnic ~~are~~ tomorrow. _____is_____

2 Jack wants to tell his friends about there adventures. _____

3 They needs some picnic food for the party. _____

4 Jack plan to wear his new T-shirt and jeans. _____

5 Jack and Dr Wild likes Kelly's orange top. _____

6 Dr Wild plans to get a new collar to Oscar. _____

2 Look and write.

Ron

Millie

Sonia

Josh

Adam

Lucy

1 _____Millie_____ is brushing her hair.

2 _____ is brushing the dog.

3 _____ is putting a collar on the dog.

4 _____ is putting a ribbon in her hair.

5 _____ is wearing a pretty top.

6 _____ is wearing smart clothes.

3 Choose and write.

top   ~~forget~~   smart   brush   collar

1 Don't ____forget____ to do your homework today!

2 You can choose what _____ to wear at the weekend.

3 Dogs must wear a _____ when they go for a walk.

4 You must _____ your teeth every morning and evening.

5 You must look _____ when you go to the party.

4 Match.

① b

②

③

④

⑤

⑥

a He's throwing the ball.

b He's going to throw the ball.

c She's phoning her friend.

d She's going to phone her friend.

e They're playing football.

f They're going to play football.

5 Write Am/Is/Are and match.

1 __Are__ they going to go on holiday?

2 _____ he going to take his laptop with him?

3 _____ we going to go to the airport?

4 _____ she going to take some photos?

5 _____ it going to rain?

6 _____ you going to phone them?

a Yes, I am.

b No, he isn't.

c Yes, they are.

d No, it isn't.

e No, we aren't.

f Yes, she is.

6 Correct the sentences.

1 Mel going to go to the picnic.   _Mel is going to go to the picnic._

2 Are they going walk there?   _____

3 I'm go to wear my new pink top.   _____

4 Jack isn't going to buys any food.   _____

5 Is you going to take your camera?   _____

6 They're going to having a wonderful time.   _____

9d SKILLS

You need to take a camera.

Writing class: writing an address 🖊

1 Write the addresses in the correct order.

1 ~~BS17 3DY~~ _____

8 Duke Street _____

Dr Sophie Wild _____

Bristol _____BS17 3DY_____

2 ~~Tower Prison~~ _____

SW25 4QZ _____Tower Prison_____

Mr M Wolf _____

London _____

Newgate Road _____

Look!

Name: Mrs A Rowley
House number: 17
Street name: Castle Road
Town or city: London
Postcode: E12 7RJ

2 Write your address.

Name: _____   Town or city: _____

House number: _____   Postcode: _____

Street name: _____   Country: _____

3 **What about you?** Write a postcard to a friend about your holiday.

- Write the address on the right and your message on the left.
- Write where you are and who you are with.

Write about

- something you saw.
- something you did.
- something you want to do.

Dear _____,

_____

I'm in _____ with

_____

_____

_____

_____

Love from _____

AIR MAIL POSTAL SERVICE
30 C 493
JULY 2011

4 Read, choose and write.

a camera   ~~a coat~~   an umbrella   some sun cream   your diary   a sun hat

1 (I think it's going to rain.)

You _____ *need to take a coat* _____.

You _____.

2 (It's going to be very hot.)

You _____.

You _____.

3 (I'm going to do some fantastic things.)

You _____.

You _____.

5 Choose and write.

How long   good idea   first visit   ~~so excited~~   Five days   pretty country

Elaine: I'm (1) _____ *so excited* _____ . We're going to the UK tomorrow.

Max: That's fantastic. Is this your (2) _____ ?

Elaine: Yes, it is.

Max: (3) _____ are you going for?

Elaine: (4) _____ .

Max: It's a (5) _____ . You need to take a video camera.

Elaine: That's a (6) _____ . Thank you.

6 Look at 5. Circle and write.

1 (a) (b) (c)

Where's Elaine going tomorrow?

_____ *She's going to the UK.* _____

2 (a) April 3rd / Sept 3rd   (b) May 15th / June 19th   (c) July 21st / July 26th

When's she going?

_____

3 (a) (b) (c)

What's she going to take?

_____

Geography

1 **Circle the words that are animals.**

(seal)   light   scientist   walrus

ice   penguin   polar bear   dark

fox   temperature   whale   continent

2 **Read and write the words you didn't circle in 1.**

1 When water is very cold, it changes to _____ice_____ .

2 In winter the days are short and _____ .

3 When you are well, your body _____ is 37°C.

4 The Antarctic is a _____ .

5 In summer the days are long and _____ .

6 Marie Curie was a Polish _____ who won two Nobel Prizes.

3 **Choose and write.**

winter snow reindeer ~~Arctic~~ skiing icy Father Christmas day forests never

My name's Aleksi and I come from Lapland in Finland. I live in Rovaniemi, a small town in the

(1) _____Arctic_____ Circle. It's famous because (2) _____ lives here. In summer it's light

all (3) _____ . In (4) _____ it's always dark and the streets are very

(5) _____ . But I like winter best because I love the (6) _____ . I can go

(7) _____ . When I'm skiing, I sometimes see wild animals. There are lots of birds and

squirrels in the (8) _____ . Wolves and foxes also live there but you (9) _____ see

them. There are (10) _____ , too. Sometimes they come into the town.

4 Read and complete.

Two hundred years ago people didn't know about the Antarctic. The first person to see the Antarctic was a captain on a Russian ship, Thaddeus Bellingshausen, in 1820. There were many expeditions to the Antarctic in the 19th century but it was a difficult place to visit.

The first people reached the South Pole in 1911. A British expedition and an expedition from Norway raced each other to the South Pole. Roald Amundsen and his Norwegian team arrived on December 14th.

A month later the British, led by Robert Scott, also reached the South Pole but the team died on the return journey.

18 years later an American called Richard E. Byrd flew a plane to the South Pole and back. In 1978 the first child, an Argentinian called Emilio Marcos Palma, was born in the Antarctic. Today the Antarctic has many visitors but people don't live there all the time.

Date	The first person ...	Name
1820	sees the Antarctic.	Captain Thaddeus Bellingshausen
	reaches the South Pole.	
	flies a plane to the South Pole.	
	is born in the Antarctic.	

5 Read and circle True or False.

1 People knew about the Antarctic a thousand years ago.   True / ~~False~~

2 The first person to see the Antarctic was on a Russian boat.   True / False

3 There weren't any expeditions to the Antarctic in the 19th century.   True / False

4 The British and the Norwegians raced to the South Pole in 1911.   True / False

5 The first person to fly to the South Pole was Argentinian.   True / False

6 Thousands of people live in the Antarctic.   True / False

6 Your project! Look and write.

Country	Australia
Landscape	• deserts • snowy mountains • rainforests
Animals	• kangaroos and koalas (only place in the world) • crocodiles • sharks

Australia is a very big country. It's also a continent.
There are _____
_____
_____
_____
_____
_____
_____
_____

Review 5

1 Look and answer.

1 Are there many swans? ___No, there aren't.___

2 Is there a bridge across the river? _____

3 Do people live next to the lake? _____

4 Is the woman good at water skiing? _____

5 Is there a person in the boat? _____

6 Is the man on the beach wearing a hat? _____

7 Does the dog look friendly? _____

8 Can the girl swim? _____

9 Is it sunny? _____

2 Read, choose and write.

wear   ask   take   ~~go~~

1 She hasn't got any money.   She ____needs to go____ to the bank.

2 It's snowy outside.   You _____ a warm coat.

3 They're going to the beach.   They _____ some sun cream.

4 He wants to go to the party.   He _____ his mum and dad.

3 Write about last year for you.

1 send a Valentine's card _I sent a Valentine's card./I didn't send a Valentine's card._

2 eat Chinese food _____

3 learn English _____

4 get taller _____

5 read lots of books _____

6 go on holiday _____

4 Write a, e, o, u and say.

We (1) _a t e_ lunch (2) ___t my sister's house. Then I drove back (3) h___r___ from (4) h___r house.
She let (5) ___s (6) ___s___ her car. I'm (7) n___t going to send a (8) n___t___ – I can phone her this evening
to say thank you.

5 Look and answer.

1 Who's the girl going to meet?

<u>She's going to meet a friend.</u>

2 Where are they going to go?

_____

3 What's the girl going to do?

_____

4 What's the boy going to do?

_____

6 Write about you.

1 At the moment I'm _____ .

2 Last year I went _____ .

3 Every morning I have to _____ .

4 I'm happy when I'm _____ .

5 At the weekend I like _____ .

6 In the summer holidays I'm going to _____ .

My English

7 Look and write. Then check and answer.

1 It's raining. You _____ to take an umbrella. ☐

2 Did you go _____ last week? ☐

3 No, we went _____ . ☐

4 We're _____ to go camping in Lapland next week. ☐

5 Who are those people? They're _____ who work in the Antarctic. ☐

How did you do? _____   **1** = OK   **2–3** = Good   **4–5** = Excellent